GEOMETRY
ANSWER KEY & TEST BANK

Greg Sabouri
Shawn Sabouri

Table of Contents

Geometry: A Teaching Textbook™
Answer Key and Test Bank
Greg Sabouri and Shawn Sabouri

Printed in the United States of America.

ISBN: 0-9749036-1-2

Teaching Textbooks, Inc.
P. O. Box 60529
Oklahoma City, OK 73146
www.teachingtextbooks.com

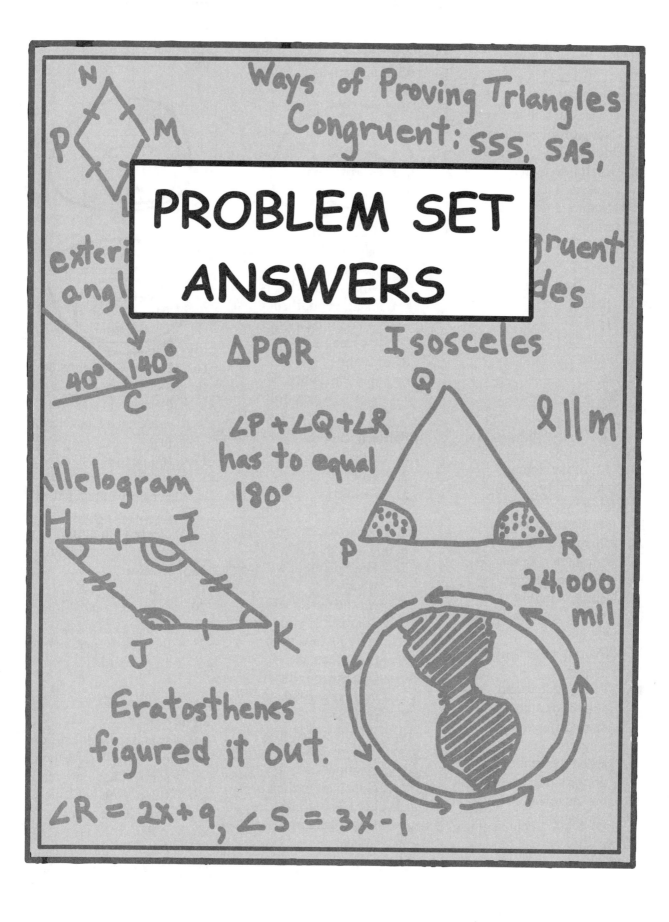

CHAPTER 1

Practice 1
a. That coin will always
b. None of the workers
c. all the sides are equal
d. Everyone in the Murdock family
e. 1 gram, 2 grams, 3 grams (or any other three different masses)

Problem Set 1
1. True
2. True
3. False
4. False
5. B
6. A
7. C
8. All of the cans
9. every time
10. All of the donuts
11. None of the students
12. every year
13. all the sides are equal
14. always equal to 1 centimeter
15. Everyone in the Burgess family
16. All the tennis balls in the basket
17. Everyone loses their money
18. 1 pound; 2 pound; 3 pound (or any other three different weights)
19. asked to see the driver's license
20. the chemical compound

Practice 2
a. Deductive
b.

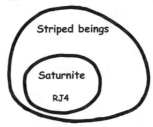

c. If a sandwich is a Dagwood, then it has salami. If Nina's sandwich is a Dagwood, then Nina's sandwich has salami.
d. Invalid
e. then Patti must be over 16 years old

Problem Set 2
1. True
2. True
3. False
4. E
5. D
6. B
7. The treatment will always
8. All the customers
9. Premise: If you run the 100 yard dash in 10 seconds
   Conclusion: then you are a good sprinter
10. Premise: If Bruce Teller wins the election
    Conclusion: then he will become mayor of Cove Creek.
11. Inductive

12. Deductive
13. Inductive
14.

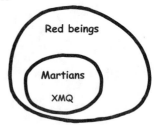

15.

16. If a car is a sports car, then it's fast. If a Corvette is a sports car, then a Corvette is fast.
17. If a person is a cowboy, then that person wears a hat. If the Lone Ranger is a cowboy, then the Lone Ranger wears a hat.
18. Invalid
19. Valid
20. then Terry must love jeans
21. then Sam must be over 18 years old

Practice 3
a. If an ice cream store is on Wylie Drive, then it serves chocolate malts.
b. If a person is Chinese, then the person is Asian. If Li is Chinese, then Li is Asian.

c. Invalid

d. *I Say Tomato, You Say Radish* was a classic.

e. Self-evident

Problem Set 3

1. True
2. True
3. False
4. Premise: If all of Salvador Dominguez's napkin drawings are great works of art
   Conclusion: then Salvador Dominguez was a great napkin drawer
5. Premise: If all the players on the team are injured
   Conclusion: then the team will have to forfeit tonight's game
6. If a pizza joint is in Melville, then it serves pepperoni.
7. If an attorney wears a robe to work, then the attorney is a judge.
8.

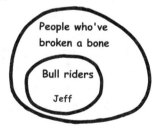

9.

10.

11. If a person is a German, then he/she is a European. If Gerhard is a German, then Gerhard is a European.
12. If a person is a philosopher, then he/she is a discussion lover. If Soren is a philosopher, then he is a discussion lover.
13. Invalid
14. Valid
15. then lots of barbecue sauce will be served Friday night
16. *As Free as the Grass Grows* was based on his travels in Africa
17. it doesn't need any film
18. Self-evident
19. Self-evident
20. Not self-evident

Practice 4

a. If a pastry is from Mel's Bakery, then it is delicious.

b. Invalid

c. Valid

d. If Dana goes shopping tomorrow, then she'll have to eat leftovers.

e. If Melanie wins her match, then she'll be in the semi-finals.
If Melanie is in the semi-finals, then she'll have to play on Saturday.
If Melanie plays on Saturday, then she'll be too tired.
If Melanie is too tired, then she'll lose in the semi-finals.

Problem Set 4

1. True
2. True
3. True
4. C
5. D
6. The bowler will always
7. Sales at the restaurant chain will rise every year
8. If you have a well-balanced diet, then your body will get the vitamins it needs.
9. If material is radioactive, then it is very dangerous.
10.

11.

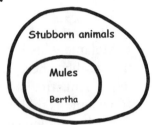

12. If a person is a thief, then he is a criminal. If a bank robber is a thief, then he is a criminal.

13. If a substance is a gas, then it is compressible. If hydrogen is a gas, then hydrogen is compressible.

14. Invalid

15. Valid

16. the medical intern is grouchy

17. the Quartet in F major, op. 135 is a masterpiece

18. If Joey's locker is empty, then he'll have to clean the garage.

19. If the sky is turbulent, then Mr. Russell will get fired.

20. If the team wins the game, they'll be in the playoffs. If the team is in the playoffs, they'll have to play in Dallas. If the team plays in Dallas, the fans will be against them. If the fans are against the team, the team will lose in the playoffs.

21. If the flowers aren't watered, they will wither.

If the flowers wither, they'll have to be thrown away. If the flowers are thrown away, they can't be shown at the wedding. If the flowers aren't shown at the wedding, the bride will be upset.

Practice 5

a.

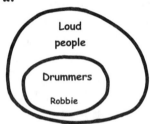

b. If a film is an animated film, then it's from the 20th century. If Snow White is an animated film, then Snow White is from the 20th century.

c. Invalid

d. Theorem: If the cat gets outside, Mom will have to sing the baby to sleep.

e. If Mrs. Johnson has the driveway redone, Mr. Johnson will get wet cement on his shoes. If Mr. Johnson gets wet cement on his shoes, he will

also get some on Mrs. Johnson's new carpet. If Mr. Johnson gets wet cement on Mrs. Johnson's new carpet, she will hit him over the head with a frying pan. If Mrs. Johnson hits Mr. Johnson over the head with a frying pan, he will have to go to the emergency room.

Problem Set 5

1. True

2. True

3. False

4. A

5. B

6. C

7. Premise: If Odysseus returns home within one year
Conclusion: then Penelope will be pleased.

8. Premise: If justice is served
Conclusion: then Lady Macbeth will be punished

9. If a car is a Rolls Royce, then it is very expensive.

10. If a train is within sight, then it's too dangerous to cross the tracks.

11.

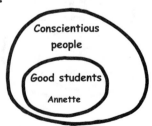

4

12.

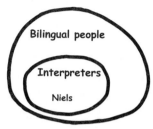

13. If a city is in Argentina, then it's in South America. If Buenos Aires is in Argentina, then it's in South America.

14. If a painter is an abstract painter, then he/she is from the 20th century. If Picasso is an abstract painter, then he is from the 20th century.

15. Invalid

16. Invalid

17. Randy has strong forearms

18. X-Y45 must orbit 24,000 miles above the earth's surface

19. Theorem: If Olga falls asleep on the private plane, thousands of ticket buyers will feel cheated.

20. Theorem: If the office water cooler is removed, then Steve's wife will no longer have a reason to make little cucumber sandwiches.

21. If Twila Glisten points to the grand prize, then the audience will say "ooh" and "ahh." If the audience says "ooh" and "ahh," then contestant #3 will get nervous. If contestant #3 gets nervous, then he will miss the question. If contestant #3 misses the question, then he will be the runner-up.

22. If the florist delivers the roses to the wrong office, Jane will think she has a secret admirer. If Jane thinks she has a secret admirer, she will make a hair appointment for tomorrow. If Jane makes a hair appointment for tomorrow, she will have to postpone her Christmas shopping again. If Jane postpones her Christmas shopping again, she will end up wrapping presents on Christmas Eve.

CHAPTER 2

Practice 6
a. Line
b. Point or plane
c. $\overleftrightarrow{AB}$
d. If a person is a tree surgeon, then he/she operates on trees.
e. Invalid

Problem Set 6
1. False
2. True
3. line
4. plane
5. line
6. line
7. point or plane
8. $\overrightarrow{LM}$
9. any lower-case letter
10. The door-to-door vacuum cleaner salesman will be rejected on all
11. All of the samples from the expedition
12. If an instrument is a violin, then it is played in an orchestra.
13. If a person is an investigative reporter, then he/she looks for corruption.
14.

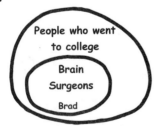

15.

16. If a house is on Elm St., then it's in Happy Valley. If Smith's house is on Elm St., then Smith's house is in Happy Valley.
17. If a book is in the library, then Myra has read it. If *War & Peace* is in the library, then Myra has read it.
18. Valid
19. Invalid
20. Invalid
21. China's economy will have recessions
22. Bobo is funny
23. If the groundhog sees its shadow, then love will not fill the air.
24. If the rebels enter the demilitarized zone tomorrow, then negotiations will break down. If negotiations break down, then the government will attack. If the government attacks, then the rebels will be crushed. If the rebels are crushed, then all hope for democracy is lost.

Practice 7
a. No
b. No
c. *S*
d. Valid
e. A country in Europe is Germany; does not pass

Problem Set 7
1. True
2. True
3. True
4. straight line
5. plane
6. No
7. No
8. Yes
9. No
10. D
11. C
12. F
13. If an egg is a Faberge egg, then it is from Russia.
14. If a pencil is at the car rental agency, then it says "Swifty Rentals."
15.

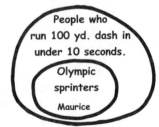

16.

17. If an office is in the Sky High building, then it is over 500 feet high. If Donald's office is in the Sky High building, then it is over 500 feet high.

18. If a person is a member of the McKinley sisters, then she has the giggles. If Lisa is a member of the McKinley sisters, then she has the giggles.

19. Invalid

20. Valid

21. Wyatt wears a white hat

22. Thurgood memorized his lines

23. A state in America is Texas; does not pass

24. A large, hairy, social bee that nests underground is a bumblebee; passes

Practice 8

a. $m\overline{HI} = 4.5$ or $HI = 4.5$

b. Yes (because $LO + OP = LP$)

c. No (because $RS + ST \neq RT$)

d. Premise: If a person is a zookeeper
Conclusion: then that person loves animals.

e. An English unit of measure that is 5,280 feet long is a mile; passes

Problem Set 8

1. True
2. True
3. Congruent
4. line segment; end points
5. line
6. plane
7. $m\overline{JK} = 2.5$ or $JK = 2.5$
8. $m\overline{CD} = 3$ or $CD = 3$
9. Yes (because $AB + BC = AC$)
10. No (because $DE + EG \neq DG$)
11. Premise: If the truck arrives by 5:30
Conclusion: then the shipment will be on time.
12. Premise: If a person is a firefighter
Conclusion: then that person is brave.
13.

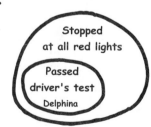

14.

15. If a person flosses, he/she will get fewer cavities. If Frank flosses, Frank will get fewer cavities.

16. If a person is an argyle sock wearer, then that person is a sock wearer. If Bitsy is an argyle sock wearer, then she is a sock wearer.

17. Invalid

18. Valid

19. Lincoln is in the United States

20. room 412 has been cleaned

21. If the auctioneer raises the bid for the painting, then Mrs. Higgins will drop out.
If Mrs. Higgins drops out, then Rutherford will win the auction.
If Rutherford wins the auction, the proceeds will go to the library.
If the proceeds go to the library, then the library will be able to build a new wing.

22. A Roman military leader was Julius Caesar; does not pass

23. An English unit of measure that is 12 inches long is a foot; passes

Practice 9

a. $\angle JKL$ or $\angle LKJ$ or $\angle K$

b. $\angle HEF$ or $\angle FEH$

c. No (because $TY + YZ \neq TZ$)

d. Invalid

e. A sales clerk at Smith's Department Store is Bitsy; does not pass

Problem Set 9
1. True
2. True
3. unique straight line
4. unique plane
5. vertex
6. sides
7. One
8. None
9. Two
10. $\angle QRS$ or $\angle SRQ$ or $\angle R$
11. $\angle 2$
12. $\angle DAB$ or $\angle BAD$
13. $m\overline{AB} = 2$ or $AB = 2$
14. $m\overline{OP} = 4.5$ or $OP = 4.5$
15.

16.

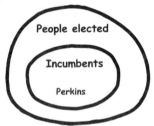

17. Yes (because $LM + MN = LN$)
18. No (because $SX + XZ \neq SZ$)
19. Invalid
20. Valid

21. Combined Consolidated Corp. rose on Tuesday
22. our next door neighbor's pet is a dog
23. The capital of the U. S. is Washington, D.C.; passes
24. A sophomore at State University is Randolph Simpson; does not pass

Practice 10
a. Line
b. $\angle MPQ$ or $\angle QPM$
c. approximately 30°
d. approximately 130°
e. Invalid

Problem Set 10
1. False
2. True
3. True
4. Congruent
5. $\overrightarrow{BO}$ is between $\overrightarrow{BA}$ and $\overrightarrow{BC}$
6. ray
7. Ray
8. Line segment
9. Angle
10. $\angle TUW$ or $\angle WUT$ or $\angle U$
11. $\angle AOC$ or $\angle COA$
12. approximately 67°
13. approximately 44°
14. approximately 114°
15.

16.

17. Valid
18. Invalid
19. he shouldn't be in a leadership position
20. he can make it through boot camp
21. If the batter hits a double, then he'll drive in one run. If the batter drives in one run, then the Tigers will win the playoffs. If the Tigers win the playoffs, then the city will celebrate. If the city celebrates, then the street cleaners will have to work overtime.
22. A hybrid offspring of a male donkey and a female horse is a mule; passes
23. A well-known author is Ralph Waldo Emerson; does not pass

Practice 11
a. 70°
b. Obtuse
c. F is between G and H
d. $\overrightarrow{OL}$ is between $\overrightarrow{OA}$ and $\overrightarrow{OB}$

e. A machine used for transportation is a Formula 1 race car; does not pass

Problem Set 11
1. True
2. False
3. acute angle
4. 90°
5. obtuse angle
6. unique straight line
7. unique plane
8. angle
9. ray
10. 120°
11. 25°
12. 95°
13. Acute
14. Obtuse
15. Obtuse
16. Yes (because $TW + WB = TB$)
17. U is between V and Q
18. $\overrightarrow{DP}$ is between $\overrightarrow{DC}$ and $\overrightarrow{DE}$
19. $\overrightarrow{SQ}$ is between $\overrightarrow{SR}$ and $\overrightarrow{ST}$
20. Invalid
21. Invalid
22. If the cat burglar leaves his flashlight, then the maid will think something is wrong.
If the maid thinks something is wrong, then she will check the safe.
If the maid checks the safe, then she will find it open.

If the maid finds the safe open, then she will faint.
23. A figure of a person made from packed snow is a snowman; passes
24. An article of clothing worn by men is a necktie; does not pass

Practice 12
a. $\overrightarrow{MK}$ is between $\overrightarrow{ML}$ and $\overrightarrow{MN}$
b. $m\overline{PQ} = 2\dfrac{1}{7}$
c. $QR = 5$
d. $m\angle QPD = 36$
e. $m\angle BCV = 28$ and $m\angle VCE = 28$

Problem Set 12
1. True
2. False
3. True
4. midpoint
5. bisector
6. bisector
7. line segment
8. Congruent
9. vertex
10. rays
11. J is between E and L
12. $\overrightarrow{UX}$ is between $\overrightarrow{UT}$ and $\overrightarrow{UV}$
13. $m\overline{ST} = 5\dfrac{1}{4}$
14. $FG = 8$
15. $JK = 3$
16. $m\angle RYZ = 48$
17. $m\angle ABD = 16$

18. $m\angle MOL = 37$ and $m\angle LOP = 37$
19. Acute
20. Acute
21. Acute
22. the last e-mail attachment should not be opened
23. Mr. McKenna was honored
24. A hanging mass of ice formed by the freezing of dripping water is an icicle; passes
25. A hard subject is calculus; does not pass

Practice 13
a. Acute
b. $UI = 6\dfrac{1}{4}$
c. $CN = 5.85$
d. $m\angle PQR = 28$
e. Invalid

Problem Set 13
1. True
2. True
3. equal; $a + c = b + c$; Addition Property
4. multiplied; equal; Multiplication Property
5. substituted; Substitution Property
6. expressions; reversed; Symmetric Property
7. acute angle
8. bisector
9. Congruent

10. Two, one, none
11. Acute
12. $\overrightarrow{QZ}$ is between $\overrightarrow{QW}$
    and $\overrightarrow{QS}$
13. $FJ = 4\frac{1}{4}$
14. $m\overline{DE} = 7.5$
15. $AP = 7.45$
16. $m\angle AOY = 23$
17. $m\angle EFG = 36$
18. Obtuse
19. Acute
20. Invalid
21. Valid
22. A famous painter was
    Leonardo da Vinci;
    does not pass
23. A self-propelled
    submarine missile is
    a torpedo; passes

CHAPTER 3

Practice 14

a. Substitution Property or Transitive Property

b. Definition of Betweenness of Points

c. $HJ = 2.5$

d. $MO = 28.2$

e. **(2)** $\overline{WO}$ bisects $\angle TOS$
   (3) $m\angle 1 = \frac{1}{2} m\angle UOR$
   (4) Definition of angle bisector
   (5) Given
   (6) $\frac{1}{2} m\angle UOR = \frac{1}{2} m\angle TOS$
   (7) Substitution Property

Problem Set 14

1. True
2. True
3. vertex
4. line
5. equal; $a = c$; Transitive Property
6. divided; $\frac{a}{c} = \frac{b}{c}$; Division Property
7. subtracted; equal; Subtraction Property
8. itself; Reflexive Property
9. Multiplication Property
10. Substitution Property or Transitive Property
11. Definition of Betweenness of Points
12. Definition of the midpoint of a line segment
13. $m\angle WNY = 59$
14. $BC = 8.9$
15. $QB = 2.7$
16. $VW = 24.6$
17. $m\angle ABW = 38$
18. $m\angle LMN = 58$
19. the old oak tree is over 10 feet tall
20. is wearing a red sweater in the Christmas card photograph
21. valid
22. valid
23. A process that occurs inside of plants is photosynthesis; does not pass
24. An important organ of the body is the kidney; does not pass
25. **(2)** $\overline{AB}$ bisects $\angle DBC$
   (3) Definition of angle bisector
   (4) $m\angle 2 = \frac{1}{2} m\angle DBC$
   (5) Given
   (6) Multiplication Property
   (7) $m\angle 1 = m\angle 2$

Practice 15

a. Substitution Property or Transitive Property; Multiplication Property

b. $\angle ADB$, $\angle BDC$, $\angle ADC$

c. $x = 2$

d. $30°$

e. **(1)** Given
   (2) Definition of Betweenness of Rays
   (3) Given
   (4) Definition of right angle
   (5) Substitution Property
   (6) Definition of complementary angles

Problem Set 15

1. False
2. True
3. obtuse angle
4. $90°$
5. Noncollinear
6. sides
7. Definition of angle bisector
8. Division Property
9. Subtraction Property
10. Substitution Property or Transitive Property; Multiplication Property
11. $\overline{GK}$, $\overline{HK}$, $\overline{IK}$, $\overline{GH}$, $\overline{HI}$, $\overline{GI}$
12. $\angle G$, $\angle I$
13. $\angle GKH$, $\angle HKI$, $\angle GKI$
14. $m\angle BPC = 38$
15. $x = 4$
16. $60°$

17. 40°
18. 40°
19.

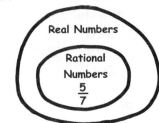

20.

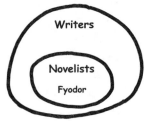

21. Invalid
22. Invalid
23. **(1)** Given
(2) Definition of Betweenness of Rays
(3) ∠ZOX is a right angle
(4) Definition of right angle
(5) Substitution Property
(6) ∠ZOY and ∠YOX are complementary

Practice 16

a. complement: $90 - y$
   supplement: $180 - y$
b. If two angles are complementary to the same angle or congruent angles, then they are congruent.
c. $x = 20$
d. $m\angle SPF = 62$; Acute

e. **(1)** $\overline{DG}$ bisects ∠EDF (Given)
(2) $m\angle 3 = m\angle 4$ (Definition of angle bisector)
(3) ∠1 and ∠3 are supplementary (Given)
(4) ∠2 and ∠4 are supplementary (Given)
(5) $m\angle 1 = m\angle 2$ (Supplements of equal angles are equal.)

Problem Set 16

1. True
2. False
3. midpoint
4. plane
5. straight line
6. complement: 65°
   supplement: 155°
7. complement: 2°
   supplement: 92°
8. complement: $90 - x$
   supplement: $180 - x$
9. Symmetric Property
10. Substitution Property
11. Betweenness of Points
12. If two angles are supplementary to the same angle, then they are congruent.
13. $x = 34$
14. $y = 37$
15. Q is between R and S
16. $\overrightarrow{MK}$ is between $\overrightarrow{MJ}$ and $\overrightarrow{ML}$
17. $y = 3$
18. $m\angle HOP = 54$; Acute

19. If a person is a latte drinker, then he is an espresso drinker. If Linda is a latte drinker, then she is an espresso drinker.
20. If a person is an author of the *Federalist*, then he was a U.S. founding father. If James Madison was an author of the *Federalist*, then he was a U.S. founding father.
21. A vehicle with a single wheel that is propelled by pedals is a unicycle; passes
22. A place to purchase clothing is a department store; does not pass
23. **(1)** $\overrightarrow{MO}$ bisects ∠NPQ (Given)
(2) $m\angle NPO = m\angle OPQ$ (Definition of angle bisector)
(3) ∠NPO and ∠NPM are supplementary (Given)
(4) ∠OPQ and ∠QPM are supplementary (Given)
(5) $m\angle QPM = m\angle NPM$ (Supplements of equal angles are equal.)

Practice 17

a. Not adjacent; don't have the same vertex

b. If two angles are a linear pair, then they are supplementary.

c. $m\angle AXB = 40$

d. $EG = 2$

e. **(1)** $\angle 5$ and $\angle 6$ are a linear pair. (Given); **(2)** $\angle 5$ and $\angle 6$ are supplementary (If two angles are a linear pair, then they are supplementary.); **(3)** $\angle 4$ and $\angle 6$ are supplementary. (Given) **(4)** $m\angle 4 = m\angle 5$ (If two angles are supplementary to same angle, they are equal.)

Problem Set 17

1. True
2. False
3. Adjacent angles
4. multiplied; equal; Multiplication Property
5. equal (congruent)
6. Not adjacent; don't have the same vertex
7. Adjacent;
8. Not adjacent; they have interior points in common (overlap).
9. Definition of the midpoint of a line segment
10. Multiplication Property
11. If two angles are a linear pair, then they are supplementary.
12. $z = 21$
13. $x = 61$
14. B is between P and R
15. $m\angle DOE = 30$
16. $m\angle IRK = 110$; Obtuse
17. $AB = 4$
18. $x = 115$
19. $y = 65$
20. $z = 115$
21. Invalid
22. Valid
23. **(1)** $\angle 2$ and $\angle 3$ are a linear pair. (Given) **(2)** $\angle 2$ and $\angle 3$ are supplementary (If two angles are a linear pair, then they are supplementary.); **(3)** $\angle 1$ and $\angle 3$ are supplementary. (Given) **(4)** $m\angle 1 = m\angle 2$ (If two angles are supplementary to equal angles, they are equal.)

Practice 18

a. Substitution Property or Transitive Property

b. $m\angle KOJ = 53$

c. $60°$

d.

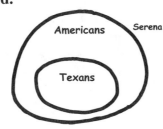

e. **(1)** $\angle ABO$ is complementary to $\angle AOB$ (Given) **(2)** $\angle CDO$ is complementary to $\angle DOC$ (Given) **(3)** $m\angle AOB = m\angle DOC$ (Pairs of vertical angles are equal) **(4)** $m\angle ABO = m\angle CDO$ (If two angles are complementary to equal angles, then they are equal.)

Problem Set 18

1. True
2. True
3. Complementary
4. bisector
5. Adjacent angles
6. line segment
7. complement: $43°$ supplement: $133°$
8. complement: $90 - 3y$ supplement: $180 - 3y$
9. If two angles are complementary to the same angle, then they are congruent.
10. Substitution Property or Transitive Property
11. Pairs of vertical angles are congruent.
12. $m\angle AOD = 49$
13. $m\angle AOB = 131$
14. $m\angle DOC = 131$
15. $33°$
16. $72°$
17. $m\angle BOC = 65$

18. $RT = 40$
19. $m\angle EOG = 58$
20. $KM = 20$
21.

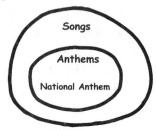

22.

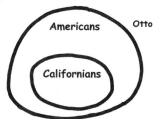

23. (1) $\angle 1$ is complementary to $\angle 3$ (Given)
    (2) $\angle 2$ is complementary to $\angle 4$ (Given)
    (3) $m\angle 1 = m\angle 2$ (Pairs of vertical angles are equal)
    (4) $m\angle 3 = m\angle 4$ (If two angles are complementary to equal angles, then they are equal.)

Practice 19
a. Perpendicular lines intersect to form 4 right angles.
b. $m\angle KOJ = 108$
c. 34°
d. $m\angle NPL = 54$
e. Valid

Problem Set 19
1. True
2. False
3. bisector
4. vertex
5. Vertical angles
6. expressions; reversed; Symmetric Property
7. divided; $\dfrac{a}{c} = \dfrac{b}{c}$; Division Property
8. Definition of complementary angles
9. Pairs of vertical angles are congruent.
10. Addition Property
11. Perpendicular lines intersect to form 4 right angles.
12. $m\angle EPF = 112$
13. $m\angle DPE = 68$
14. 56°
15. 69°
16. $PB = 21$
17. $m\angle SQT = 63$
18. If a person is an NBA player, then he is not short.
19. If a person is a Barker, then he/she is not a musician.
20. Valid
21. Valid
22. (1) $m\angle 1 = m\angle 4$ (Given)
    (2) $m\angle 1 = m\angle 2$ (Vertical angles are equal.)
    (3) $m\angle 3 = m\angle 4$ (Vertical angles are equal.)
    (4) $m\angle 4 = m\angle 2$ (Substitution or Transitive Property)
    (5) $m\angle 2 = m\angle 3$ (Substitution or Transitive Property).

Practice 20
a. Substitution Property and Division Property
b. $m\angle HKL = 72$
c. 121°
d.

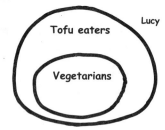

e. Invalid

Problem Set 20
1. False
2. False
3. $\overleftrightarrow{ST}$ is not perpendicular to $\overline{CE}$.
4. $\overleftrightarrow{BV}$ and $\overleftrightarrow{FG}$ cannot both be perpendicular to $\overleftrightarrow{AB}$.
5. perpendicular bisector
6. Adjacent angles
7. Supplementary
8. midpoint
9. If two angles are a linear pair, then they are supplementary.
10. Subtraction Property
11. Substitution Property and Division Property

12. complement: 69°
    supplement: 159°
13. complement: $2x$
    supplement: $90 + 2x$
14. $m\angle ABC = 84$
15. $m\angle BEF = 64$
16. 75°
17. 137°
18.

Clap for food

Walruses

Whiskers

19.

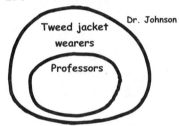

Tweed jacket wearers   Dr. Johnson

Professors

20. Invalid
21. Invalid
22. (1) $\overline{AC} \perp \overline{BC}$
    (2) $\angle 1$ and $\angle 2$ are adjacent
    (3) Definition of right angle
    (4) Betweenness of Rays
    (5) $m\angle 1 + m\angle 2 = 90$ (Substitution).

Practice 21

a. If the exterior sides of a pair of adjacent angles are perpendicular, then the angles are complementary.
b. $m\angle MOL = 60$

c. 105°
d. always
e. (1) $\overline{LM} \perp \overline{MN}$, $\overline{PN} \perp \overline{MN}$, $\angle 5 \cong \angle 8$ (Given);
    (2) $\angle 5$ is complementary to $\angle 6$ and $\angle 7$ is complementary to $\angle 8$ (If the exterior sides of a pair of adjacent angles are perpendicular, then the angles are complementary.)
    (3) $\angle 6 \cong \angle 7$ (If two angles are complementary to congruent angles, then they are congruent.)

Problem Set 21

1. True
2. True
3. Supplementary
4. vertical
5. perpendicular
6. complementary
7. approximately $1\frac{3}{4}$ inches
8. approximately 1 inch
9. approximately $\frac{1}{2}$ inch
10. If two angles are supplementary to the same angle, then they are congruent.
11. Betweenness of Points
12. If the exterior sides of a pair of adjacent angles are

perpendicular, then the angles are complementary.
13. $m\angle FOG = 35$
14. $m\angle JOI = 35$
15. 25°
16. 141°
17. sometimes
18. always
19. never
20. $m\angle XQZ = 72$
21. $AB = 32$
22. Invalid
23. Valid
24. (1) $\overline{FJ} \perp \overline{FG}$, $\overline{GH} \perp \overline{FG}$, $\angle 2 \cong \angle 4$ (Given)
    (2) $\angle 1$ is complementary to $\angle 2$ and $\angle 3$ is complementary to $\angle 4$ (If the exterior sides of a pair of adjacent angles are perpendicular, then the angles are complementary.)
    (3) $\angle 1 \cong \angle 3$ (If two angles are complementary to congruent angles, then they are congruent.)

CHAPTER 4

Practice 22

a. $\angle 1$ and $\angle 6$, $\angle 2$ and $\angle 5$

b. $m\angle QKE = 80$

c. $m\angle F = 99$

d. $m\angle LKN = 78$

e. If a person is a poison ivy victim, then that person itches a lot. If Sam does not itch a lot, then Sam is not a poison ivy victim.

Problem Set 22

1. True
2. False
3. transversal
4. lines EF and GH are parallel.
5. perpendicular
6. acute angle
7. $\angle 3$ and $\angle 6$, $\angle 4$ and $\angle 5$
8. $\angle 7$ and $\angle 3$, $\angle 8$ and $\angle 4$, $\angle 5$ and $\angle 1$, $\angle 6$ and $\angle 2$
9. No; no; no
10. Multiplication Property
11. Vertical angles are congruent.
12. Transitive or Substitution Property
13. All right angles are congruent.
14. sometimes
15. always
16. $m\angle LNO = 40$
17. $m\angle KLN = 100$
18. $m\angle ADS = 62$
19. $m\angle J = 116$

20. $GI = 31$
21. $m\angle APC = 86$
22. If a person is a pirate, then that person is a scumbag. If Captain Hook is a pirate, then Captain Hook is a scumbag.
23. If a creature is a possum, then that creature is a furry critter. If a goldfish is not a furry critter, then the goldfish is not a possum.
24. (1) Given
    (2) Given
    (3) $\angle 1 \cong \angle 3$, $\angle 2 \cong \angle 4$
    (4) $\angle 1 \cong \angle 2$
    (6) Transitive (or Substitution)
    (7) If the exterior sides of adjacent angles are perpendicular, then the angles are complementary.
    (8) $\angle 6$ is complementary to $\angle 4$.
    (9) $\angle 5 \cong \angle 6$ (If two angles are complementary to congruent angles, then the angles are congruent.)

Practice 23

a. Corresponding angles; alternate interior angles

b. Subtraction Property; Substitution Property

c. $m\angle EFP = 115$

d. $26°$, $64°$

e. (1) $\overline{AD} \parallel \overline{BC}$, $\overline{AB} \parallel \overline{DC}$ (Given);
   (2) $m\angle 6 = m\angle 4$, $m\angle 5 = m\angle 3$ (If two parallel lines are cut by a transversal, then alternate interior angles are equal.)
   (3) $m\angle 6 + m\angle 5 = m\angle 4 + m\angle 3$ (Addition Property);
   (4) $m\angle ABC = m\angle 5 + m\angle 6$ and $m\angle ADC = m\angle 3 + m\angle 4$ (Betweenness of Rays)
   (5) $m\angle ABC = m\angle ADC$ (Substitution Property).

Problem Set 23

1. True
2. True
3. perpendicular bisector
4. Complementary angles
5. itself; Reflexive Property
6. obtuse angle
7. Supplementary angles; alternate interior angles
8. Supplementary angles; vertical angles
9. Corresponding angles; vertical angles
10. Addition Property
11. Definition of midpoint

12. Subtraction Property; Substitution Property
13. $m\angle AOB = 60$
14. $m\angle COQ = 60$
15. $m\angle GOI = 57$
16. $CT = 92$
17. $m\angle AOB = 26$
18. $32°$, $58°$
19. $36°$
20. Valid
21. Invalid
22. **(1)** $\angle AOB$ and $\angle BOC$ are a linear pair (Given)
    (2) $m\angle AOB + m\angle BOC = 180$. (If two angles are a linear pair, then they are supplementary.);
    (3) $m\angle AOB = m\angle BOC$. (Given);
    (4) $m\angle AOB + m\angle AOB = 180$ or $2m\angle AOB = 180$ (Substitution)
    (5) $m\angle AOB = 90$ (Division)
    (6) $m\angle BOC = 90$ (Substitution)
    (7) $\angle AOB$ and $\angle BOC$ are right angles. (Definition of right angle).
23. **(1)** $\overline{DE} \parallel \overline{GF}$, $\overline{EF} \parallel \overline{DG}$ (Given);
    (2) $m\angle 1 = m\angle 4$, $m\angle 2 = m\angle 3$ (If two parallel lines are cut by a transversal, then alternate interior angles are equal.)
    (3) $m\angle 1 + m\angle 2 = m\angle 4 + m\angle 3$ (Addition Property);

(4) $m\angle EDG = m\angle 1 + m\angle 2$ and $m\angle EFG = m\angle 3 + m\angle 4$ (Betweenness of Rays)
(5) $m\angle EDG = m\angle EFG$ (Substitution Property).

Practice 24

a. Corresponding angles; congruent
b. If two parallel lines are cut by a transversal, alternate exterior angles are congruent.
c. $m\angle 3 = 35$
d. $m\angle S = 118$
e. **(1)** $\overline{DE} \parallel \overline{FG}$ $\angle D \cong \angle E$ (Given);
   (2) $\angle D$ and $\angle DFG$ are supplementary (If parallel lines are cut by a transversal, then interior angles on the same side of the transversal are supplementary.)
   (3) $\angle E$ and $\angle EGF$ are supplementary (If parallel lines are cut by a transversal, then interior angles on the same side of the transversal are supplementary.)
   (4) $\angle DFG \cong \angle EGF$ (If two angles are supplementary to congruent angles, then they are congruent.)

Problem Set 24

1. False
2. False
3. Supplementary
4. transversal
5. vertex
6. equal; $a = c$; Transitive Property
7. Corresponding angles; congruent
8. Interior angles on same side of transversal; supplementary
9. Adjacent angles (linear pair); supplementary
10. If two parallel lines are cut by a transversal, alternate exterior angles are congruent.
11. If two parallel lines are cut by a transversal, alternate interior angles are congruent.
12. If two parallel lines are cut by a transversal, interior angles on the same side of the transversal are supplementary.
13. sometimes
14. always
15. $m\angle 2 = 32$
16. $m\angle 3 = 36$
17. $m\angle D = 112$
18. $MN = 14$
19. $m\angle IOJ = 57$
20. $60°$
21. $69°$, $111°$
22. **(1)** $\overline{PT} \parallel \overline{WV}$, $\overline{RQ} \parallel \overline{SU}$ (Given);

(2) $\angle 1 \cong \angle MTW$ (If parallel lines are cut by a transversal, then corresponding angles are congruent.); $\angle 2 \cong \angle MTW$ (If parallel lines are cut by a transversal, then alternate interior angles are congruent.) **(3)** $\angle 1 \cong \angle 2$ (Transitive Property).

23. **(1)** $\overline{CP} \parallel \overline{QL}$
$\angle Q \cong \angle L$ (Given);
(2) $\angle C$ and $\angle Q$ are supplementary (If parallel lines are cut by a transversal, then interior angles on the same side of the transversal are supplementary.)
(3) $\angle P$ and $\angle L$ are supplementary (If parallel lines are cut by a transversal, then interior angles on the same side of the transversal are supplementary.)
(4) $\angle C \cong \angle P$ (If two angles are supplementary to congruent angles, then they are congruent.)

Practice 25
a. Alternate interior angles; congruent
b. $x = 61$
c. $138°$, $42°$
d. Invalid

e. **(1)** $\overline{GH} \parallel \overline{KL}$, $\overline{IH}$ bisects $\angle GHK$, $\overline{JK}$ bisects $\angle HKL$ (Given)
(2) $m\angle GHI = \frac{1}{2}m\angle GHK$ and $m\angle JKL = \frac{1}{2}m\angle HKL$ (Definition of angle bisector)
(3) $m\angle GHK = m\angle HKL$ (If parallel lines are cut by a transversal, alternate interior angles are congruent.)
(4) $\frac{1}{2}m\angle GHK = \frac{1}{2}m\angle HKL$ (Multiplication)
(5) $m\angle GHI = m\angle JKL$ (Substitution)

Problem Set 25
1. False
2. True
3. congruent
4. complementary
5. perpendicular bisector
6. supplementary
7. Transitive Property
8. Definition of segment bisector
9. Transitive or Substitution Property
10. Vertical angles; congruent
11. Alternate interior angles; congruent
12. Alternate interior angles; congruent

13. $x = 67$
14. $m\angle QPR = 90$
15. $m\angle DSE = 41$
16. $KP = 58$
17. $m\angle AOB = 41$
18. $15°$
19. $128°$, $52°$
20. Valid
21. Invalid
22. **(1)** $\overline{MN} \parallel \overline{PQ} \parallel \overline{SR}$, $\overline{MR} \parallel \overline{ST}$ (Given);
(2) $\angle 1 \cong \angle QPR$ (If parallel lines are cut by a transversal, corresponding angles are congruent.)
(3) $\angle QPR \cong \angle PRS$ (If parallel lines are cut by a transversal, alternate interior angles are congruent.)
(4) $\angle 1 \cong \angle PRS$ (Transitive)
(5) $\angle PRS \cong \angle 2$ (If parallel lines are cut by a transversal, alternate interior angles are congruent.)
(6) $\angle 1 \cong \angle 2$ (Transitive).

23. **(1)** $\overline{AB} \parallel \overline{FE}$, $\overline{BC}$ bisects $\angle ABE$, $\overline{DE}$ bisects $\angle BEF$ (Given)
(2) $m\angle ABC = \frac{1}{2}m\angle ABE$ and $m\angle DEF = \frac{1}{2}m\angle BEF$ (Definition of angle bisector)

18

(3) $m\angle ABE$
$= m\angle BEF$ (If parallel lines are cut by a transversal, alternate interior angles are congruent.)
(4) $\frac{1}{2}m\angle ABE$
$= \frac{1}{2}m\angle BEF$ (Multiplication)
(5) $m\angle ABC$
$= m\angle DEF$ (Substitution)

Practice 26

a. If two lines form congruent alternate interior angles with a transversal, then the lines are parallel.
b. $x = 51$
c. Invalid (because second statement is converse of first)
d. If an animal has feathers, then it is a peacock; Converse is not true and definition is bad.
e. **(1)** $\angle O \cong \angle U$,
    $\overline{SO} \parallel \overline{WU}$ (Given);
    (2) $\angle S \cong \angle U$ (If two parallel lines are cut by a transversal, then their alternate interior angles are congruent.)
    (3) $\angle O \cong \angle S$ (Transitive or Substitution)
    (4) $\overline{AO} \parallel \overline{SU}$ (If two lines form congruent alternate interior

angles with a transversal, then the lines are parallel.)

Problem Set 26

1. True
2. True
3. parallel
4. $a \leftrightarrow b$
5. congruent
6. midpoint
7. If two parallel lines are cut by a transversal, then interior angles on the same side of the transversal are supplementary.
8. If two angles are complementary to the same angle, then they are congruent.
9. If two lines form congruent alternate interior angles with a transversal, then the lines are parallel.
10. Interior angles on the same side of the transversal; supplementary
11. Alternate interior angles; congruent
12. Linear pair; supplementary
13. $x = 32$
14. $y = 48$
15. $JP = 82$
16. $m\angle ECF = 48$
17. $m\angle A = 119$
18. Valid
19. Invalid (because second statement is converse of first)

20. If a person plans buildings and oversees their construction, then he is an architect; Converse is true and definition is good
21. If an animal has a bushy tail, then it is a raccoon; Converse is not true and definition is bad
22. **(1)** $\angle E \cong \angle G$,
    $\overline{DE} \parallel \overline{FG}$ (Given);
    (2) $\angle E \cong \angle F$ (If two parallel lines are cut by a transversal, then their alternate interior angles are congruent.)
    (3) $\angle F \cong \angle G$ (Transitive or Substitution)
    (4) $\overline{EF} \parallel \overline{GH}$ (If two lines form congruent alternate interior angles with a transversal, then the lines are parallel)

Practice 27

a. If Akio lives in Japan, then he lives in Tokyo; False
b. If two lines form congruent alternate interior angles with a transversal, then the lines are parallel.
c. $y = 29$
d. $m \parallel n$
e. $33°$

Problem Set 27

1. True
2. True
3. congruent; parallel
4. interior: supplementary
5. complementary
6. acute
7. If Shelley lives in United States, then she lives in the Arizona; False
8. If the measure of two angles is 180°, then the angles are supplementary.; True
9. If two angles are congruent, then they are vertical; False
10. If two lines form congruent alternate interior angles with a transversal, then the lines are parallel.
11. Pairs of vertical angles are congruent.
12. Multiplication Property
13. sometimes
14. always
15. $x = 25$
16. $y = 22$
17. $o \parallel p$
18. $\ell \parallel m$
19. None
20. $\ell \parallel n$
21. 36°
22. 42°
23. **(1)** Given
    (2) $\angle DFE$ is complementary to $\angle DEG$
    (3) $m\angle DEF = 90$
    (5) Substitution Property
    (6) Subtraction Property
    (7) Definition of complementary angles
    (8) If two angles are complementary to the same angle, then they are congruent.
    (9) $\overleftrightarrow{DF} \parallel \overleftrightarrow{GH}$ (If two lines form congruent alternate interior angles with a transversal, then the lines are parallel.

CHAPTER 5

Practice 28

a. Included sides: $\overline{AB}$ and $\overline{AC}$; opposite side: $\overline{BC}$.

b. $m\angle IMN = 70$

c. Interior angles on the same side of the transversal; supplementary

d. $OD = 23$

e. **(1)** $\angle F \cong \angle S$, $m\angle H + m\angle S = 180$ (Given)
(2) $m\angle H + m\angle F = 180$ (Substitution)
(3) $\overline{FR} \parallel \overline{HS}$ (If two lines form supplementary interior angles on the same side of a transversal, then the lines are parallel.)

Problem Set 28

1. False
2. True
3. transversal
4. sides; angles
5. congruent
6. supplementary
7. Concave
8. Convex
9. Included sides: $\overline{AB}$ and $\overline{BC}$; opposite side: $\overline{AC}$.
10. Included angles: $\angle A$ and $\angle B$; opposite angle: $\angle C$.
11. If the exterior sides of a pair of adjacent angles are perpendicular, then the angles are complementary.
12. Pairs of vertical angles are congruent.
13. If two lines form congruent alternate exterior angles with a transversal, then the lines are parallel.
14. sometimes
15. sometimes
16. $m\angle ACB = 82$
17. $m\angle CEF = 68$
18. Alternate interior angles; congruent
19. Interior angles on the same side of the transversal; supplementary
20. $m\angle WDY = 89$
21. $TR = 49$
22. If a person knows how to use chopsticks, then he is from China; Converse is false and definition is bad.
23. If a polygon has three sides, then it is a triangle; Converse is true and definition is good.
24. **(1)** $\angle D \cong \angle L$, $m\angle G + m\angle L = 180$ (Given)
(2) $m\angle G + m\angle D = 180$ (Substitution)
(3) $\overline{DP} \parallel \overline{GL}$ (If two lines form supplementary interior angles on the same side of a transversal, then the lines are parallel.)

Practice 29

a. Scalene triangle; Right triangle

b. Legs: $\overline{BL}$ and $\overline{LC}$; Hypotenuse: $\overline{BC}$

c. $y = 54$

d. $40°$

e. **(1)** $d \parallel f$, $f \parallel g$ (Given)
(2) $\angle 1 \cong \angle 4$ (If two parallel lines are cut by a transversal, then their alternate interior angles are congruent.)
(3) $\angle 4 \cong \angle 8$ (If two parallel lines are cut by a transversal, then their corresponding angles are congruent.)
(4) $\angle 1 \cong \angle 8$ (Transitive)
(5) $d \parallel g$ (If two lines form congruent alternate interior angles with a transversal, then the lines are parallel.)

Problem Set 29

1. True
2. False
3. no
4. $90°$
5. equilateral
6. obtuse
7. Included sides: $\overline{RS}$ and $\overline{SQ}$; opposite side: $\overline{RQ}$.

8. Included angles: $\angle S$ and $\angle Q$; opposite angle: $\angle R$.

9. Scalene triangle; Right triangle

10. Legs: $\overline{AJ}$ and $\overline{DJ}$; Hypotenuse: $\overline{AD}$

11. Addition Property

12. Definition of Midpoint

13. $\ell \parallel m$

14. None

15. $x = 30$

16. $y = 51$

17. $36°$

18. $72°$

19.

20.

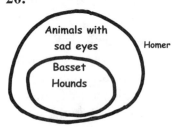

21. If a triangle has all sides with different lengths, then it is scalene; True

22. If a triangle has two equal sides, then it is isosceles; True

23. (1) $m \parallel n$, $n \parallel q$ (Given)
    (2) $\angle 2 \cong \angle 3$ (If two parallel lines are cut by a transversal, then their alternate interior angles are congruent.)
    (3) $\angle 3 \cong \angle 7$ (If two parallel lines are cut by a transversal, then their corresponding angles are congruent.)
    (4) $\angle 2 \cong \angle 7$ (Transitive)
    (5) $m \parallel q$ (If two lines form congruent alternate interior angles with a transversal, then the lines are parallel.)

24. (1) $m\angle 1 + m\angle 3 = 180$ (Given)
    (2) $m\angle 1 = m\angle 2$ (Pairs of vertical angles are congruent.)
    (3) $m\angle 2 + m\angle 3 = 180$ (Substitution)
    (4) $\angle 2$ and $\angle 3$ are supplementary (Definition of supplementary angles)
    (5) $t \parallel r$ (If two lines form supplementary interior angles on the same side of a transversal, then the lines are parallel.)

Practice 30

a. $55°$, $60°$, $65°$; acute

b. The sum of the measures of the angles of a triangle is 180.

c. $x = 25$, $y = 80$

d. Valid

e. (1) $\overline{AB} \perp \overline{AE}$ (Given)
   (2) $\angle A$ is a right angle. (Definition of perpendicular lines)
   (3) $\triangle ABE$ is a right triangle. (Definition of right triangle)
   (4) $\angle B$ and $\angle E$ are complementary. (The acute angles of a right triangle are complementary.)
   (5) $m\angle B + m\angle E = 90$ (Definition of complementary angles)

Problem Set 30

1. True
2. True
3. $180°$
4. equiangular
5. acute
6. isosceles
7. sometimes
8. always
9. never
10. $30°$, $60°$, $90°$
11. $45°$, $45°$, $90°$
12. $50°$, $60°$, $70°$; acute
13. If two lines form congruent alternate interior angles with a transversal, then the lines are parallel.
14. If two parallel lines are cut by a transversal, then interior angles on the same side of the transversal are supplementary.

15. The sum of the measures of the angles of a triangle is 180.
16. $x = 30$, $y = 75$
17. $x = 40$, $y = 40$
18. $x = 130$, $y = 60$
19. $AC = 19$
20. $m\angle 3 = 35$
21. Valid
22. Invalid
23. (1) $\angle C \cong \angle L$ (Given)
    (2) $\angle VBC \cong \angle LBG$ (Pairs of vertical angles are congruent.)
    (3) $\angle V \cong \angle G$ (If two angles of a triangle are congruent to two angles of another triangle, then the remaining pair of angles are congruent.)
24. (1) $\overline{RT} \perp \overline{ST}$ (Given)
    (2) $\angle T$ is a right angle. (Definition of perpendicular lines)
    (3) ΔRST is a right triangle. (Definition of right triangle)
    (4) $\angle R$ and $\angle S$ are complementary. (The acute angles of a right triangle are complementary.)
    (5) $m\angle R + m\angle S = 90$ (Definition of complementary angles)

Practice 31

a. 30°
b. 125°
c. Not possible
d. 72°
e. (1) $\overline{BV} \perp \overline{VG}$, $\overline{GP} \perp \overline{PZ}$ (Given)
   (2) $\angle V$ and $\angle P$ are right angles. (Perpendicular lines intersect to form right angles)
   (3) $\angle V \cong \angle P$ (All right angles are congruent.)
   (4) $\angle 3$ and $\angle 4$ are vertical angles. (Given)
   (5) $\angle 3 \cong \angle 4$ (Pairs of vertical angles are congruent.)
   (6) $\angle B \cong \angle Z$ (If two angles of a triangle are congruent to two angles of another triangle, then the remaining pair of angles are congruent.)

Problem Set 31

1. False
2. True
3. legs
4. congruent
5. supplementary
6. equal to; two
7. 30°, 60°, 90°; right triangle
8. 60°, 60°, 60°
9. 10°, 80°, 90°
10. If two angles are a linear pair, then they are supplementary

11. If two parallel lines are cut by a transversal, then their alternate interior angles are congruent.
12. If two parallel lines are cut by a transversal, then their corresponding angles are congruent.
13. $x = 112$
14. $x = 120$
15. 37°
16. 65°
17.

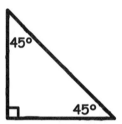

18. Not possible
19. 69°
20. 60°
21. If a triangle has three sides, then it is obtuse; Converse is false and definition is bad.
22. If a triangle has one angle with a measure of 90°, then it is a right triangle; Converse is true and definition is good.
23. (1) $\overline{AD} \perp \overline{AF}$, $\overline{FC} \perp \overline{CH}$ (Given)
    (2) $\angle A$ and $\angle C$ are right angles. (Perpendicular lines intersect to form right angles)
    (3) $\angle A \cong \angle C$ (All right angles are congruent.)

(4) $\angle 1$ and $\angle 2$ are vertical angles. (Given)
(5) $\angle 1 \cong \angle 2$ (Pairs of vertical angles are congruent.)
(6) $\angle D \cong \angle H$ (If two angles of a triangle are congruent to two angles of another triangle, then the remaining pair of angles are congruent.)

Practice 32

a. $\overline{AH} \cong \overline{IU}$, $\overline{HE} \cong \overline{UQ}$, $\overline{AE} \cong \overline{IQ}$
b. $\overline{YN}$
c. $x = 20$, $y = 100$
d. $x = 15$, $y = 136$
e. **(1)** $\angle 4$ is an exterior angle of ΔIKL (Given)
(2) $m\angle 4 = m\angle L + m\angle 6$ (Exterior Angle of a Triangle Theorem)
(3) $m\angle 4 - m\angle 6 = m\angle L$ (Subtraction)
(4) $m\angle L = m\angle 4 - m\angle 6$ (Symmetric)

Problem Set 32

1. True
2. True
3. corresponding angles; corresponding sides
4. six
5. complementary

6. congruent; parallel
7. $\angle J \cong \angle D$, $\angle K \cong \angle F$, $\angle L \cong \angle G$
8. $\overline{JK} \cong \overline{DF}$, $\overline{KL} \cong \overline{FG}$, $\overline{JL} \cong \overline{DG}$
9. RPS
10. $\angle P$
11. $\overline{PS}$
12. never
13. always
14. The sum of the measures of the angles of a triangle is $180°$.
15. If two lines form congruent alternate interior angles with a transversal, then the lines are parallel.
16. If two lines form supplementary interior angles on the same side of a transversal, then the lines are parallel.
17. $x = 35$, $y = 95$
18. $x = 25$, $y = 105$
19. $x = 23$, $y = 128$
20. $m\angle BOC = 50$
21. $DG = 48$
22. **(1)** ΔDFH and ΔEGI are equiangular. (Given)
(2) $m\angle D = 60$ and $m\angle EGI = 60$ (The measure of each angle of an equiangular triangle is 60.).
(3) $\angle D \cong \angle EGI$ (Substitution).

23. **(1)** : $\angle 1$ is an exterior angle of ΔURS. (Given)
(2) $m\angle 1 = m\angle R + m\angle 3$ (Exterior Angle of a Triangle Theorem)
(3) $m\angle 1 - m\angle 3 = m\angle R$ (Subtraction)
(4) $m\angle R = m\angle 1 - m\angle 3$ (Symmetric)

Practice 33

a. Side-Angle-Side Postulate
b. $m\angle K = 72$, $m\angle JDK = 72$
c. $x = 30$, $y = 120$
d. $36°$
e. **(1)** $\angle HFG \cong \angle IHF$; J is the midpoint of $\overline{FH}$; $\overline{FG} \cong \overline{HI}$ (Given)
(2) $\overline{HJ} \cong \overline{FJ}$ (Definition of midpoint)
(3) $\Delta FGJ \cong \Delta HIJ$ (S.A.S.)

Problem Set 33

1. True
2. True
3. one line
4. congruent
5. equal to; two
6. obtuse
7. $\angle H \cong \angle K$, $\angle S \cong \angle L$, $\angle U \cong \angle P$
8. $\overline{HS} \cong \overline{KL}$, $\overline{SU} \cong \overline{LP}$, $\overline{HU} \cong \overline{KP}$

9. Not possible
10. Draw any triangle with all unequal sides and all angles measuring less than $90°$.
11. Exterior Angle of a Triangle Theorem
12. Side-Angle-Side Postulate
13. Side-Angle-Side Postulate
14. $38°$, $52°$, $90°$
15. $25°$, $25°$, $130°$
16. $x = 30$, $y = 50$
17. $m\angle S = 60$, $m\angle TRS = 75$
18. $x = 45$, $y = 135$
19. $53°$
20. $45°$
21. If all three of the angles of a triangle are congruent, then the triangles are congruent; false
22. If a triangle has one angle that measures less than $90°$, then it is acute; false
23. (1) $\angle BAD \cong \angle ADC$; E is the midpoint of $\overline{AD}$; $\overline{AB} \cong \overline{CD}$ (Given)
    (2) $\overline{AE} \cong \overline{ED}$ (Definition of midpoint)
    (3) $\triangle ABE \cong \triangle DCE$ (S.A.S.)

Practice 34

a. $\overline{BX}$
b. Angle-Angle-Side Theorem
c. Invalid
d. $x = 30$
e. 1) $\overline{HD} \perp \overline{FH}$, $\overline{FP} \perp \overline{PD}$, $\angle 3 \cong \angle 4$. (Given)
   (2) $\angle H$ and $\angle P$ are right angles. (Perpendicular lines intersect to form right angles.)
   (3) $\angle H \cong \angle P$. (All right angles are congruent.)
   (4) $\overline{FD} \cong \overline{FD}$. (Reflexive Property)
   (5) $\triangle HDF \cong \triangle FPD$ (Angle-Angle-Side Theorem)

Problem Set 34

1. True
2. False
3. isosceles
4. congruent
5. complementary
6. interior; supplementary
7. $\overline{RP}$
8. $\angle P$
9. $\overline{LP}$
10. $\angle K$
11. always
12. never
13. Transitive (or Substitution) Property
14. If two angles of one triangle are congruent to two angles of another triangle, then the third pair of angles are congruent.
15. Angle-Angle-Side Theorem
16. Valid
17. Invalid
18. $x = 130$
19. $x = 18$
20. $x = 36$
21. $ER = 21$
22. $m\angle A = 134$
23. (1) $\overline{IG} \perp \overline{IK}$, $\overline{GM} \perp \overline{KM}$, $\angle 1 \cong \angle 2$. (Given)
    (2) $\angle I$ and $\angle M$ are right angles. (Perpendicular lines intersect to form right angles.)
    (3) $\angle I \cong \angle M$. (All right angles are congruent.)
    (4) $\overline{GK} \cong \overline{GK}$. (Reflexive Property)
    (5) $\triangle GKI \cong \triangle KGM$ (Angle-Angle-Side Theorem)

Practice 35

a. Substitution Property
b. Hypotenuse-Leg
c. $x = 47$
d. $x = 118$
e. (1) $\overline{NL} \perp \overline{MO}$, $\overline{PQ} \perp \overline{MO}$ (Given)
   (2) $\angle MLN$ and $\angle OQP$ are right angles (Perpendicular lines intersect to form right angles.)
   (3) $\triangle MLN$ and $\triangle OQP$ are right triangles (Definition of right triangle)
   (4) $MQ = ML + QL$ and $OL = OQ + QL$

(Betweenness of Points)

(5) $MQ = OL$ (Given)

(6) $ML + QL = OQ + QL$ (Substitution)

(7) $ML = OQ$ (Subtraction)

(8) $MN = PO$ (Given)

(9) $\triangle MLN \cong \triangle OQP$ (Hypotenuse-Leg)

Problem Set 35

1. False
2. True
3. congruent
4. perpendicular bisector
5. equilateral
6. acute
7. $\overline{RT}$
8. $\angle RYT$
9. $\overline{RY}$
10. Addition Property
11. Substitution Property
12. Hypotenuse-Leg
13. $o \parallel q$
14. $\ell \parallel n$
15. $45°$, $45°$, $90°$
16. $108°$, $54°$, $18°$; obtuse
17. $x = 30$, $y = 30$
18. $x = 40$
19. $x + y = 230$
20. $y = 115$
21. $56°$
22. $63°$, $117°$
23. **(1)** $\overline{HL} \perp \overline{GI}$
    $\overline{JK} \perp \overline{GI}$ (Given)

(2) $\angle GLH$ and $\angle IKJ$ are right angles (Perpendicular lines intersect to form right angles.)

(3) $\triangle GLH$ and $\triangle IKJ$ are right triangles (Definition of right triangle)

(4) $GK = GL + LK$ and $LI = IK + LK$ (Betweenness of Points)

(5) $GK = LI$ (Given)

(6) $GL + LK = IK + LK$ (Substitution)

(7) $GL = IK$ (Subtraction)

(8) $GH = JI$ (Given)

(9) $\triangle GLH \cong \triangle IKJ$ (Hypotenuse-Leg)

24. **(2)** If two parallel lines are cut by a transversal, then their alternate interior angles are congruent.

(4) Given

(5) Addition Property

(6) Substitution Property

(7) $\overline{VT} \parallel \overline{RS}$

(8) If two parallel lines are cut by a transversal, then their alternate interior angles are congruent.

(9) $\triangle QRS \cong \triangle UVT$ (Angle-Side-Angle Theorem)

Practice 36

a. Side-Side-Side

b. $x = 4$, $y = 5$
c. $y = 84$
d. $m\angle M = 29$, $m\angle MRE = 61$
e. **(1)** $\overline{RS} \cong \overline{WU}$, T is the midpoint of $\overline{RW}$ (Given)

(2) $\overline{RT} \cong \overline{TW}$ (Definition of midpoint)

(3) $\overline{ST} \cong \overline{TV}$, $\overline{TU} \cong \overline{TV}$ (Given)

(4) $\overline{ST} \cong \overline{TU}$ (Transitive or Substitution)

(5) $\triangle SRT \cong \triangle UWT$ (S.S.S.)

Problem Set 36

1. True
2. True
3. congruent
4. equal to; two
5. no
6. congruent
7. $\overline{GJ}$
8. $\angle J$
9. $\overline{TG}$
10. sometimes
11. always
12. Angle-Angle-Side
13. Side-Side-Side
14. If two parallel lines are cut by a transversal, then their alternate interior angles are congruent.
15. $m\angle E = 90$, $m\angle D = 55$, $m\angle F = 35$
16. $x = 2$, $y = 1$
17. $x = 123$

18. $y = 20$
19. $x = 85$
20. $m\angle P = 35$, $m\angle PQC = 55$
21. If the sum of the measures of two angles is $180°$, then the angles are supplementary; true
22. If two angles are supplementary, then they are a linear pair; false.
23. (1) $\overline{AC}$ bisects $\angle BAD$ and $\angle BCD$ (Given)
    (2) $\angle BAC \cong \angle DAC$ and $\angle BCA \cong \angle ACD$ (Definition of angle bisector)
    (3) $\overline{AC} \cong \overline{AC}$ (Reflexive Property)
    (4) $\triangle ABC \cong \triangle ADC$ (A.S.A.)
24. (1) $\overline{LK} \cong \overline{NP}$, M is the midpoint of $\overline{KP}$ (Given)
    (2) $\overline{KM} \cong \overline{MP}$ (Definition of midpoint)
    (3) $\overline{LM} \cong \overline{OM}$, $\overline{MN} \cong \overline{OM}$ (Given)
    (4) $\overline{LM} \cong \overline{MN}$ (Transitive or Substitution)
    (5) $\triangle LKM \cong \triangle NPM$ (S.S.S.)

Practice 37

a. $\angle DIY$
b. $r = p + q - 180$
c. $z = 21$

d. $18°$
e. (1) $\triangle HJD$ is equilateral (Given)
   (2) $\overline{HD} \cong \overline{HJ}$ (Definition of equilateral triangle)
   (3) F is the midpoint of $\overline{JD}$ (Given)
   (4) $\overline{JF} \cong \overline{FD}$ (Definition of midpoint)
   (5) $\overline{HF} \cong \overline{HF}$ (Reflexive Property)
   (6) $\triangle DFH \cong \triangle JFH$ (S.S.S)

Problem Set 37

1. True
2. False
3. two sides; angle
4. hypotenuse
5. supplementary
6. congruent
7. $\angle U$
8. $\overline{LR}$
9. $\angle URL$
10. $m\overline{NO} = 11$
11. $m\overline{VT} = x$, $m\overline{BT} = x$
12. An isosceles triangle has two congruent (equal) sides.
13. The sum of the measures of the angles of a triangle is 180.
14. The measure of the exterior angle of a triangle is equal to the sum of the measures of the two remote interior angles.
15. $x = 75$

16. $z = x + y - 180$
17. $y = 10$
18. $y = 22$
19. $m\angle FEH = 92$
20. $MB = 74$
21. $60°$
22. $64°$
23. (1) $\angle A \cong \angle E$, $\overline{AC} \cong \overline{EC}$ (Given)
    (2) $\angle C \cong \angle C$ (Reflexive)
    (3) $\triangle CAD \cong \triangle CEB$ (A.S.A.)
24. (1) $\triangle GPK$ is equilateral (Given)
    (2) $\overline{GK} \cong \overline{PK}$ (Definition of equilateral triangle)
    (3) L is the midpoint of $\overline{GP}$ (Given)
    (4) $\overline{GL} \cong \overline{LP}$ (Definition of midpoint)
    (5) $\overline{LK} \cong \overline{LK}$ (Reflexive Property)
    (6) $\triangle GLK \cong \triangle PLK$ (S.S.S)

CHAPTER 6

Practice 38

a. A.S.A
b. Corresponding Parts of Congruent Triangles are Congruent (C.P.C.T.C.)
c. $x = 34$
d. Valid
e. (1) $\overline{UV} \parallel \overline{BW}$, $\overline{AW} \parallel \overline{BV}$ (Given)
(2) $\angle UBV \cong \angle BAW$, $\angle U \cong \angle ABW$ (If two parallel lines are cut by a transversal, then corresponding angles are congruent.)
(3) $\overline{AW} \cong \overline{BV}$ (Given)
(4) $\triangle ABW \cong \triangle BUV$ (A.A.S.)

Problem Set 38

1. True
2. False
3. Side-Side-Side
4. parallel
5. congruent
6. 180
7. sometimes
8. never
9. $o \parallel q$
10. $\ell \parallel n$
11. S.A.S.
12. Hypotenuse-Leg
13. A.S.A.
14. Definition of angle bisector
15. Corresponding Parts of Congruent

Triangles are Congruent (C.P.C.T.C.)
16. Corresponding Parts of Congruent Triangles are Congruent (C.P.C.T.C.)
17. $x = 105$, $y = 40$
18. $y = 32$
19. $x = 35$
20. $y = 114$
21. Invalid
22. Valid
23. (1) $\overline{RT} \parallel \overline{PK}$, $\overline{JK} \parallel \overline{PT}$ (Given)
(2) $\angle RPT \cong \angle PJK$, $\angle R \cong \angle JPK$ (If two parallel lines are cut by a transversal, then corresponding angles are congruent.)
(3) $\overline{JK} \cong \overline{PT}$ (Given)
(4) $\triangle JPK \cong \triangle PRT$ (A.A.S.)
24. (1) Given
(2) C.P.C.T.C.
(3) Substitution
(4) $\overline{BC} \cong \overline{EF}$, $\overline{LM} \cong \overline{EF}$
(5) Substitution
(6) C.P.C.T.C.
(7) $\overline{AC} \cong \overline{KM}$
(8) S.S.S.

Practice 39

a. none
b. Definition of segment bisector
c. C.P.C.T.C.
d. $b = 142 - a$

e. (1) $\overline{AB} \perp \overline{AE}$, $\overline{ED} \perp \overline{AE}$ (Given)
(2) $\angle BAC$ and $\angle DEC$ are right angles. (Perpendicular lines intersect to form right angles.)
(3) $\angle BAC \cong \angle DEC$ (All right angles are congruent.)
(4) $\angle B \cong \angle D$, $\overline{BC} \cong \overline{CD}$ (Given)
(5) $\triangle BAC \cong \triangle DEC$ (A.A.S.)
(6) $\overline{AC} \cong \overline{EC}$ (C.P.C.T.C.)
(7) C is the midpoint of $\overline{AE}$. (Definition of midpoint)

Problem Set 39

1. True
2. True
3. right angle
4. Angle-Side-Angle
5. legs
6. congruent; congruent
7. $\overline{CH}$
8. $\angle QHD$
9. $\overline{HQ}$
10. $\angle CHQ$
11. S.A.S.
12. none
13. C.P.C.T.C.
14. Definition of segment bisector
15. C.P.C.T.C.
16. Definition of angle bisector
17. $y = 26$
18. $x = 35$
19. $x = 37$
20. $y = 138 - x$

21. 135°
22. 15°
23. **(1)** $\overline{AO} \cong \overline{CO}$, $\overline{AB} \cong \overline{CB}$ (Given)
    (2) $\overline{BO} \cong \overline{BO}$ (Reflexive)
    (3) $\triangle ABO \cong \triangle CBO$ (S.S.S.)
    (4) $\angle ABO \cong \angle CBO$ (C.P.C.T.C.)
    (5) $\overline{BO}$ bisects $\angle ABC$ (Definition of angle bisector)
24. **(1)** $\overline{FD} \perp \overline{DH}$, $\overline{JH} \perp \overline{DH}$ (Given)
    (2) $\angle FDG$ and $\angle JHG$ are right angles. (Perpendicular lines intersect to form right angles.)
    (3) $\angle FDG \cong \angle JHG$ (All right angles are congruent.)
    (4) $\angle F \cong \angle J$, $\overline{FG} \cong \overline{JG}$ (Given)
    (5) $\triangle FDG \cong \triangle JHG$ (A.A.S.)
    (6) $\overline{DG} \cong \overline{HG}$ (C.P.C.T.C.)
    (7) G is the midpoint of $\overline{DH}$. (Definition of midpoint)

Practice 40

a. C.P.C.T.C.
b. If two angles in a linear pair have equal measures, then each is a right angle.
c. $x = 9$, $y = 29$
d. $x = 17$, $y = 16$

e. **(1)** $\overline{JG} \parallel \overline{KM}$, $\overline{JG} \cong \overline{KM}$, $\overline{HJ} \cong \overline{JK}$ (Given)
   (2) $\angle HJG \cong \angle JKM$ (If two parallel lines are cut by a transversal, then corresponding angles are congruent.)
   (3) $\triangle GHJ \cong MJK$ (S.A.S.)
   (4) $\angle H \cong \angle KJM$ (C.P.C.T.C.)
   (5) $\overline{HG} \parallel \overline{JM}$ (If two lines form congruent corresponding angles with a transversal, then the lines are parallel.)

Problem Set 40

1. True
2. True
3. corresponding angles; corresponding sides
4. Angle-Angle-Side
5. interior; supplementary
6. equilateral
7. sometimes
8. always
9. 25°, 75°, 80°; acute
10. 110°, 45°, 25°; obtuse
11. C.P.C.T.C.
12. If two lines form alternate interior angles with a transversal, then the lines are parallel.
13. If two angles in a linear pair have equal measures, then each is a right angle.
14. A.A.S.
15. Hypotenuse-Leg
16. $x = 142$
17. $x = 13$, $y = 55$
18. $x = 39$, $y = 88$
19. $x = 14$, $y = 19$
20. If a triangle has one angle that is less than 90°, then it is obtuse; false
21. If two triangles are congruent, then all three of their corresponding angles and all three of their corresponding sides are congruent; true
22. **(1)** $\overline{MT} \cong \overline{LT}$, $\overline{OT}$ is a bisector of $\angle MTL$ (Given)
    (2) $\angle MTO \cong \angle OTL$ (Definition of angle bisector)
    (3) $\overline{OT} \cong \overline{OT}$ (Reflexive)
    (4) $\triangle MTO \cong \triangle OTL$ (S.A.S.)
    (5) $\angle MOT \cong \angle LOT$ (C.P.C.T.C.)
    (6) $\angle MOT$ and $\angle LOT$ are a linear pair. (Definition of linear pair)
    (7) $\angle MOT$ and $\angle LOT$ are right angles. (If two angles in a linear pair are congruent, then each is a right angle.)
    (8) $\overline{OT} \perp \overline{LM}$ (Definition of perpendicular lines.)

23. **(1)** $\overline{BE} \parallel \overline{CD}$,
$\overline{BE} \cong \overline{CD}$, $\overline{AE} \cong \overline{ED}$
(Given)
(2) $\angle BEA \cong \angle CDE$
(If two parallel lines
are cut by a
transversal, then
corresponding angles
are congruent.)
(3) $\triangle ABE \cong \triangle ECD$
(S.A.S.)
(4) $\angle A \cong \angle CED$
(C.P.C.T.C.)
(5) $\overline{AB} \parallel \overline{CE}$ (If two
lines form congruent
corresponding angles
with a transversal,
then the lines are
parallel.)

Practice 41
a. altitude
b.

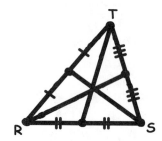

c. $x = 56$, $y = 28$,
$z = 64$
d. $30°$, $150°$
e. **(1)** $\overline{MF}$ is the
perpendicular
bisector of $\overline{DE}$
(Given)
(2) $\overline{MF} \perp \overline{DE}$,
$\overline{DM} \cong \overline{ME}$
(Definition of per-
pendicular bisector)

(3) $\angle DMF$ and
$\angle EMF$ are right
angles. (Perpen-
dicular lines intersect
to form right angles.)
(4) $\angle DMF \cong \angle EMF$
(All right angles are
congruent.)
(5) $\overline{MF} \cong \overline{MF}$
(Reflexive)
(6) $\triangle FDM \cong \triangle FEM$
(S.A.S.)
(7) $\overline{FD} \cong \overline{FE}$
(C.P.C.T.C.)

Problem Set 41
1. False
2. False
3. three; three
4. perpendicular
bisector
5. Side-Side-Side
6. sum; remote
7. median
8. altitude
9.

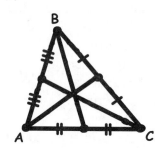

10.

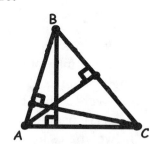

11. Angle-Side-Angle
12. None

13. The measure of an
exterior angle of a
triangle is equal to
the sum of the
measures of the two
remote interior
angles.
14. If two angles are a
linear pair, then they
are supplementary.
15. $x = 125$, $y = 75$
16. $x = 58$, $y = 29$,
$z = 60$
17. $x = 47$, $y = 27$
18. $x = 59$, $y = 31$
19. Valid
20. Invalid
21. $30°$, $60°$
22. $80°$, $100°$
23. **(1)** $\overline{BX}$ is the perpendicular bisector of
$\overline{AC}$. (Given)
(2) $\overline{BX} \perp \overline{AC}$,
$\overline{AX} \cong \overline{XC}$
(Definition of per-
pendicular bisector)
(3) $\angle BXC$ and
$\angle BXA$ are right
angles. (Perpendic-
ular lines intersect to
form right angles.)
(4) $\angle BXC \cong \angle BXA$
(All right angles are
congruent.)
(5) $\overline{BX} \cong \overline{BX}$
(Reflexive)
(6) $\triangle ABX \cong \triangle CBX$
(S.A.S.)
(7) $\overline{AB} \cong \overline{BC}$
(C.P.C.T.C.)
24. **(3)** Reflexive
(4) S.S.S.
(5) $\angle BXA \cong \angle BXC$

(6) Definition of linear pair

(7) If the two angles in a linear pair are congruent, then each is a right angle.

(8) $\overline{BX} \perp \overline{AC}$

Practice 42

a. 30°, 40°, 110°; obtuse triangle

b. 40°, 70°, 70°

c. $y = 84$

d. $y = 30$

e. **(1)** $\overline{PN} \cong \overline{PK}$; $\overline{NM} \cong \overline{LK}$ (Given)
(2) $\angle N \cong \angle K$ (Base Angles Theorem)
(3) $\angle 3 \cong \angle 4$ (Given)
(4) $\angle NOM$ and $\angle 3$ are a linear pair; $\angle LQK$ and $\angle 4$ are a linear pair (Definition of linear pair)
(5) $\angle NOM$ and $\angle 3$ are supplementary; $\angle LQK$ and $\angle 4$ are supplementary (If two angles are a linear pair, then they are supplementary.)
(6) $\angle NOM \cong \angle LQK$ (If two angles are supplementary to congruent angles, then they are congruent.)
(7) $\triangle NMO \cong \triangle KLQ$ (A.A.S.)
(8) $\overline{MO} \cong \overline{LQ}$ (C.P.C.T.C.)

Problem Set 42

1. True
2. True
3. equiangular
4. median
5. altitude
6. complementary
7. $\angle ECF$
8. $\overline{FE}$
9. $\triangle CEB$
10. 15°, 75°, 90°; right triangle
11. 50°, 65°, 65°
12. Angle-Side-Angle
13. C.P.C.T.C.
14. If the two angles in a linear pair are congruent, then each is a right angle.
15. Angle-Angle-Side
16. None
17. $x = 72$
18. $x = 76$
19. $x = 65$, $y = 64$
20. $y = 48$
21.

22.

23. **(1)** $\triangle PEG$, $\overline{EP} \cong \overline{EG}$, altitudes $\overline{PK}$ and $\overline{GH}$ (Given)
(2) $\angle PHG$ and $\angle GKP$ are right angles (Definition of altitude)
(3) $\angle PHG \cong \angle GKP$ (All right angles are congruent.)
(4) $\angle HPG \cong \angle KGP$ (Base Angles Theorem)
(5) $\overline{PG} \cong \overline{PG}$ (Reflexive)
(6) $\triangle PHG \cong \triangle GKP$ (A.A.S.)
(7) $\overline{PK} \cong \overline{GH}$ (C.P.C.T.C.)

24. **(1)** $\overline{DF} \cong \overline{AF}$; $\overline{DC} \cong \overline{AB}$ (Given)
(2) $\angle A \cong \angle D$ (Base Angles Theorem)
(3) $\angle 1 \cong \angle 2$ (Given)
(4) $\angle DEC$ and $\angle 1$ are a linear pair; $\angle BGA$ and $\angle 2$ are a linear pair (Definition of linear pair)
(5) $\angle DEC$ and $\angle 1$ are supplementary; $\angle BGA$ and $\angle 2$ are supplementary (If two angles are a linear pair, then they are supplementary.)
(6) $\angle DEC \cong \angle BGA$ (If two angles are supplementary to congruent angles, then they are congruent.)
(7) $\triangle ABG \cong \triangle DCE$ (A.A.S.)

(8) $\overline{CE} \cong \overline{BG}$
(C.P.C.T.C.)

Practice 43

a. Converse of Base Angles Theorem

b. $z = 7$

c. $x = 8$

d. $126°$, $54°$

e. **(1)** $\overline{AB} \cong \overline{BC}$; $\overline{JC}$ and $\overline{KA}$ are medians of $\triangle ABC$ (Given)
(2) J is the midpoint of $\overline{AB}$ and K is the midpoint of $\overline{BC}$. (Definition of median)
(3) $AJ = \frac{1}{2} AB$ and $KC = \frac{1}{2} BC$ (Definition of midpoint)
(4) $\frac{1}{2} AB = \frac{1}{2} BC$ (Multiplication Property)
(5) $AJ = KC$ or $\overline{AJ} \cong \overline{KC}$ (Substitution)
(6) $\angle BAC \cong \angle BCA$ (Base Angles Theorem)
(7) $\overline{AC} \cong \overline{AC}$ (Reflexive)
(8) $\triangle JAC \cong \triangle KCA$ (S.A.S.)
(9) $\overline{JC} \cong \overline{KA}$ (C.P.C.T.C.)

Problem Set 43

1. True
2. True
3. $60°$
4. perpendicular bisector
5. Hypotenuse-Leg; right; right
6. $\angle PDE$
7. $\angle PDE$ and $\angle PED$
8. $\overline{ED}$
9. $\overline{ED}$ and $\overline{ET}$
10.

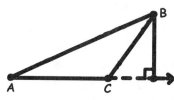

11.

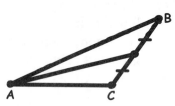

12. Base Angles Theorem
13. Converse of Base Angles Theorem
14. If two triangles are congruent to the same triangle, then they are congruent to each other.
15. $x = 15$, $y = 60$
16. $x = 35$, $y = 20$
17. $y = 6$
18. $x = 5$
19. $72°$
20. $114°$, $66°$
21. If a triangle is equiangular, then it is also equilateral; true
22. If two angles of a triangle are congruent (equal), then the sides opposite those angles are congruent (equal); true
23. **(1)** $\overline{WT} \cong \overline{TU}$; $\overline{RU}$ and $\overline{SW}$ are medians of $\triangle WTU$ (Given)
(2) R is the midpoint of $\overline{TW}$ and S is the midpoint of $\overline{TU}$. (Definition of median)
(3) $RW = \frac{1}{2} WT$ and $US = \frac{1}{2} TU$. (Definition of midpoint)
(4) $\frac{1}{2} WT = \frac{1}{2} TU$ (Multiplication Property)
(5) $RW = US$ or $\overline{RW} \cong \overline{US}$ (Substitution)
(6) $\angle TWU \cong TUW$ (Base Angles Theorem)
(7) $\overline{WU} \cong \overline{WU}$ (Reflexive)
(8) $\triangle RWU \cong \triangle SUW$ (S.A.S.)
(9) $\overline{RU} \cong \overline{SW}$ (C.P.C.T.C.)

24. **(1)** $\overline{PS} \cong \overline{QS}$ (Given)
(2) $\angle 2 \cong \angle 3$ (Base Angles Theorem)
(3) $\angle 1$, $\angle 2$ and $\angle 3$, $\angle 4$ are linear pairs (Definition of linear pair)
(4) $\angle 1$, $\angle 2$ and $\angle 3$, $\angle 4$ are supplementary (If two angles are a linear pair, then they are supplementary.)

(5) $\angle 1 \cong \angle 4$ (If two angles are supplementary to congruent angles, then they are congruent.)

(6) $\overline{DP} \cong \overline{LQ}$ (Given)

(7) $\triangle DPS \cong \triangle LQS$ (S.A.S.)

(8) $\overline{DS} \cong \overline{LS}$ (C.P.C.T.C.)

(9) $\triangle DSL$ is isosceles (Definition of an isosceles triangle)

CHAPTER 7

Practice 44

a. $m\angle JKL > m\angle MKP$

b. (1) $-8x \geq -24$ (Addition Property of Inequality)
(2) $x \leq 3$ (Division Property of Inequality)

c. Whole Greater than Its Part Property

d. $z = 30$

e. (1) $\overline{FB} \perp \overline{AC}$, $\overline{FE} \perp \overline{AD}$ (Given)
(2) $\angle DEF$ and $\angle CBF$ are right angles. (Perpendicular lines intersect to form right angles.)
(3) ΔDEF and ΔCBF are right triangles. (Definition of right triangle)
(4) $\overline{FB} \cong \overline{FE}$, F is the midpoint of $\overline{CD}$. (Given)
(5) $\overline{DF} \cong \overline{CF}$ (Definition of midpoint)
(6) $\Delta DEF \cong \Delta CBF$ (Hypotenuse-Leg)
(7) $\angle D \cong \angle C$ (C.P.C.T.C.)
(8) $\overline{AD} \cong \overline{AC}$ (Converse of Base Angles Theorem)
(9) ΔCAD is isosceles. (Definition of isosceles triangle)

Problem Set 44

1. False
2. True
3. multiplying; dividing
4. $a > c$; Transitive Property of Inequality
5. $a + c > b + d$; Addition Property of Inequality
6. Base Angles Theorem
7. $OC < AD$
8. $m\angle DBA > m\angle OBC$
9. $m\angle CBA < m\angle OBA$
10. (1) $5x \leq 15$ (Subtraction Property of Inequality)
(2) $x \leq 3$ (Division Property of Inequality)
11. (1) $-6x \geq -12$ (Addition Property of Inequality)
(2) $x \leq 2$ (Division Property of Inequality)
12. 40°, 60°, 80°; acute
13. 110°, 35°, 35°
14. Subtraction Property of Inequality
15. Multiplication Property of Inequality
16. Whole Greater than Its Part Property
17. None
18. Hypotenuse-Leg
19. $x = 41$
20. $y = 21$
21. $x = 82$, $y = 15$
22. $x = 126$, $y = 54$
23. (1) $\angle D \cong \angle H$, $\overline{DF} \cong \overline{HF}$ (Given)
2) $\angle F \cong \angle F$ (Reflexive)
(3) $\Delta DGF \cong \Delta HEF$ (A.S.A.)
(4) $\overline{DG} \cong \overline{HE}$ (C.P.C.T.C.)

24. (1) $\overline{YS} \perp \overline{RT}$, $\overline{YU} \perp \overline{RV}$ (Given)
(2) $\angle VUY$ and $\angle TSY$ are right angles. (Perpendicular lines intersect to form right angles.)
(3) ΔVUY and ΔTSY are right triangles. (Definition of right triangle)
(4) $\overline{YS} \cong \overline{YU}$, Y is the midpoint of $\overline{TV}$. (Given)
(5) $\overline{VY} \cong \overline{TY}$ (Definition of midpoint)
(6) $\Delta VUY \cong \Delta TSY$ (Hypotenuse-Leg)
(7) $\angle V \cong \angle T$ (C.P.C.T.C.)
(8) $\overline{RV} \cong \overline{RT}$ (Converse of Base Angles Theorem)
(9) ΔTRV is isosceles. (Definition of isosceles triangle)

Practice 45

a. Yes

b. Triangle Inequality Postulate

c. $x = 52$

d. 140°, 40°

e. (1) $\overline{TR} \cong \overline{TS}$, $\overline{AT}$ bisects $\angle RTS$ (Given)
(2) $\angle RTU \cong \angle STU$ (Definition of angle bisector)

(3) $\overline{TU} \cong \overline{TU}$
(Reflexive)
(4) $\triangle RTU \cong \triangle STU$
(S.A.S.)
(5) $\overline{RU} \cong \overline{SU}$
(C.P.C.T.C.)
(6) $\angle RUT \cong \angle SUT$
(C.P.C.T.C.)
(7) $\angle RUT$ and
$\angle RUA$ are supplementary; $\angle SUT$
and $\angle SUA$ are supplementary (If two
angles are a linear
pair, then they are
supplementary.)
(8) $\angle RUA \cong \angle SUA$
(If two angles are
supplementary to
congruent angles,
then they are
congruent.)
(9) $\overline{UA} \cong \overline{UA}$
(Reflexive)
(10) $\triangle RUA \cong \triangle SUA$
(S.A.S.)

Problem Set 45
1. True
2. False
3. Converse of Base
   Angles Theorem
4. $a > b$; Division
   Property of
   Inequality
5. median
6. $WS > WQ$
7. $m\angle QSW < m\angle WQS$
8. **(1)** $12y < 84$
   (Addition Property of
   Inequality)
   (2) $y < 7$ (Division
   Property of
   Inequality)

9. **(1)** $-\dfrac{1}{2}x > 8$
   (Subtraction Property
   of Inequality)
   (2) $x < -16$
   (Multiplication Property of Inequality)
10. Yes
11. No
12. Yes
13. Whole Greater than
    Its Part Property
14. Triangle Inequality
    Postulate
15. S.S.S.
16. A.A.S.
17. $x = 66$
18. $y = 46$
19. $x = 40$, $y = 40$
20. $x = 15$, $y = 20$
21. $56°$
22. $163°$, $17°$
23. **(1)** $\overline{EA} \cong \overline{EU}$
    (Given)
    (2) $\angle 1 \cong \angle 3$ (Base
    Angles Theorem)
    (3) $\overline{AU} \parallel \overline{IO}$ (Given)
    (4) $\angle 1 \cong \angle 2$ and
    $\angle 3 \cong \angle 4$ (If two
    parallel lines are cut
    by a transversal, then
    corresponding angles
    are congruent.)
    (5) $\angle 2 \cong \angle 3$
    (Transitive or
    Substitution)
    (6) $\angle 2 \cong \angle 4$
    (Transitive or
    Substitution)
    (7) $\overline{IE} \cong \overline{OE}$
    (Converse of Base
    Angles Theorem)

(8) $\triangle IEO$ is isosceles
(Definition of
isosceles triangle)
24. **(1)** $\overline{FG} \cong \overline{FH}$, $\overline{FK}$
    bisects $\angle HFG$
    (Given)
    (2) $\angle GFJ \cong \angle HFJ$
    (Definition of angle
    bisector)
    (3) $\overline{FJ} \cong \overline{FJ}$
    (Reflexive)
    (4) $\triangle GFJ \cong \triangle HFJ$
    (S.A.S.)
    (5) $\overline{GJ} \cong \overline{HJ}$
    (C.P.C.T.C.)
    (6) $\angle GJF \cong \angle HJF$
    (C.P.C.T.C.)
    (7) $\angle GJF$ and
    $\angle GJK$ are supplementary; $\angle HJF$
    and $\angle HJK$ are supplementary (If two
    angles are a linear
    pair, then they are
    supplementary.)
    (8) $\angle GJK \cong \angle HJK$
    (If two angles are
    supplementary to
    congruent angles,
    then they are
    congruent.)
    (9) $\overline{JK} \cong \overline{JK}$
    (Reflexive)
    (10) $\triangle GJK \cong \triangle HJK$
    (S.A.S.)

Practice 46
a. Exterior Angle
   Inequality Theorem
b. $x = 70$, $y = 35$
c. $y = 72$
d. $ST = 13$, $TU = 13$

e. **(1)** $\overline{GH} \parallel \overline{IJ}$, $\overline{GH} \cong \overline{IJ}$, $\overline{GK} \cong \overline{IL}$ (Given)
(2) $\angle HGK \cong \angle JIL$ (If two parallel lines are cut by a transversal, then alternate interior angles are congruent.)
(3) $\triangle HGK \cong \triangle JIL$ (S.A.S.)
(4) $\overline{HK} \cong \overline{JL}$ (C.P.C.T.C.)
(5) $GK = IL$ (Congruent segments have equal lengths.)
(6) $GK + KL = IL + LK$ (Addition)
(7) $GK + KL = GL$ and $IL + LK = IK$ (Betweenness of Points)
(8) $GL = IK$ or $\overline{GL} \cong \overline{IK}$ (Substitution)
(9) $\angle HKG \cong \angle JLI$ (C.P.C.T.C.)
(10) $\angle HKG$ and $\angle HKI$ are supplementary; $\angle JLI$ and $\angle JLG$ are supplementary (If two angles are a linear pair, then they are supplementary.)
(11) $\angle HKI \cong \angle JLG$ (If two angles are supplementary to congruent angles, then they are congruent.)
(12) $\triangle HKI \cong \triangle JLG$ (S.A.S.)

(13) $\angle IHK \cong \angle GJL$ (C.P.C.T.C.)

Problem Set 46
1. True
2. True
3. sum; greater than
4. congruent
5. equiangular
6. always
7. never
8. No
9. Yes
10. 20°, 20°, 140°
11. 90°, 45°, 45°
12. Definition of Midpoint
13. Converse of Base Angles Theorem
14. Exterior Angle Inequality Theorem
15. $x = 65$, $y = 105$
16. $x = 50$, $y = 20$
17. $x = 40$, $y = 50$
18. $x = 15$, $y = 75$
19. $m\angle H = 19$, $m\angle K = 71$
20. $DE = 11$, $EF = 11$
21. Invalid
22. Valid
23. **(1)** $\overline{BA} \perp \overline{PA}$, $\overline{CD} \perp \overline{PD}$ (Given)
(2) $\angle BAP$ and $\angle CDP$ are right angles. (Perpendicular lines intersect to form right angles.)
(3) $\angle BAP \cong \angle CDP$ (All right angles are congruent.)
(4) $\angle APB \cong \angle DPC$ (Pairs of vertical angles are congruent.)

(5) Point P is the midpoint of $\overline{BC}$. (Given)
(6) $\overline{BP} \cong \overline{CP}$ (Definition of midpoint)
(7) $\triangle BAP \cong \triangle CDP$ (A.A.S.)
(8) $\overline{AP} \cong \overline{DP}$ (C.P.C.T.C.)
(9) $\overline{BC}$ bisects $\overline{AD}$. (Definition of segment bisector)

24. **(1)** $\overline{AB} \parallel \overline{CD}$, $\overline{AB} \cong \overline{CD}$, $\overline{AE} \cong \overline{CF}$ (Given)
(2) $\angle BAE \cong \angle DCF$ (If two parallel lines are cut by a transversal, alternate interior angles are congruent.)
(3) $\triangle BAE \cong \triangle DCF$ (S.A.S.)
(4) $\overline{BE} \cong \overline{DF}$ (C.P.C.T.C.)
(5) $AE = CF$ (Congruent segments have equal lengths.)
(6) $AE + EF = CF + EF$ (Addition)
(7) $AE + EF = AF$ and $CF + EF = CE$ (Betweenness of Points)
(8) $AF = CE$ or $\overline{AF} \cong \overline{CE}$ (Substitution)
(9) $\angle BEA \cong \angle DFC$ (C.P.C.T.C.)
(10) $\angle BEA$ and $\angle BEC$ are supplementary;

∠DFC and ∠DFA are supplementary (If two angles are a linear pair, then they are supplementary.)
(11) ∠BEC ≅ ∠DFA (If two angles are supplementary to congruent angles, then they are congruent.)
(12) ΔBEC ≅ ΔDFA (S.A.S.)
(13) ∠CBE ≅ ∠ADF (C.P.C.T.C.)

Practice 47

a. Greater than 4 and less than 16

b. $y = \dfrac{180 - 4x}{5}$

c. $y = \dfrac{3x}{2}$

d. 40°, 140°

e. **(1)** $\overline{KM} \perp \overline{NL}$, ∠3 is not ≅ to ∠4. (Given)
(2) Either $\overline{KM}$ is not the median to side $\overline{NL}$ or $\overline{KM}$ is the median to side $\overline{NL}$. Assume $\overline{KM}$ is the median to side $\overline{NL}$. (A statement is either true or false.)
(3) $\overline{NM} \cong \overline{ML}$ (Definition of median)
(4) ∠KMN and ∠KML are right angles (Perpendicular

lines intersect to form right angles.)
(5) ∠KMN ≅ ∠KML (All right angles are congruent.)
(6) $\overline{KM} \cong \overline{KM}$ (Reflexive)
(7) ΔKMN ≅ ΔKML (S.A.S.)
(8) ∠3 ≅ ∠4 (C.P.C.T.C.)
(9) $\overline{KM}$ is not the median to side $\overline{NL}$. (Statement 8 contradicts the given statement that ∠3 is not ≅ to ∠4. The assumption made in statement 2 must be false. By elimination, statement 9 must be true.)

Problem Set 47

1. True
2. False
3. Base Angles Theorem
4. Exterior Angle Inequality Theorem
5. $a = b$; Substitution Property of Inequality
6. Greater than 2 and less than 28
7. Greater than 13 and less than 23
8. **(1)** $9x + 4 \le 22$ (Addition Property of Inequality)
   (2) $9x \le 18$ (Subtraction Property of Inequality)

(3) $x \le 2$ (Division Property of Inequality)
9. **(1)** $-4y - 1 \ge 0$ (Addition Property of Inequality)
   (2) $-4y \ge 1$ (Addition Property of Inequality)
   (3) $y \le -\dfrac{1}{4}$ (Division Property of Inequality)
10. Triangle Inequality Postulate
11. Exterior Angle Inequality Theorem
12. Exterior Angle of a Triangle Theorem
13. None
14. Side-Side-Side
15. $x = 13$, $y = 11$
16. $y = \dfrac{180 - 5x}{2}$
17. $y = 47$
18. $y = 5z$
19. 32°, 58°
20. 108°, 72°
21.

22.

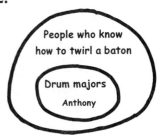

23. **(1)** $\overline{EF} \cong \overline{GF}$ (Given)
(2) $m\angle 1 = m\angle 2$ (Base Angles Theorem)
(3) $m\angle 3 > m\angle 2$ (Exterior Angle Inequality Theorem)
(4) $m\angle 3 > m\angle 1$ (Substitution)

24. **(1)** $\overline{DB} \perp \overline{AC}$, $\angle 1$ is not $\cong$ to $\angle 2$ (Given)
(2) Either $\overline{DB}$ is not the median to side $\overline{AC}$ or $\overline{DB}$ is the median to side $\overline{AC}$. Assume $\overline{DB}$ is the median to side $\overline{AC}$. (A statement is either true or false.)
(3) $\overline{AB} \cong \overline{BC}$ (Definition of median)
(4) $\angle DBA$ and $\angle DBC$ are right angles (Perpendicular lines intersect to form right angles.)
(5) $\angle DBA \cong \angle DBC$ (All right angles are congruent.)
(6) $\overline{DB} \cong \overline{DB}$ (Reflexive)
(7) $\triangle DBA \cong \triangle DBC$ (S.A.S.)
(8) $\angle 1 \cong \angle 2$ (C.P.C.T.C.)
(9) $\overline{DB}$ is not the median to side $\overline{AC}$. (Statement 8 contradicts the given statement that $\angle 1$ is not $\cong$ to $\angle 2$. The

assumption made in statement 2 must be false. By elimination, statement 9 must be true.)

Practice 48

a. Contrapositive
b. Converse: If a triangle has one angle measuring $60°$, then it is equiangular; false
Inverse: If a triangle is not equiangular, then it does not have one angle measuring $60°$; false
Contrapositive: If a triangle does not have one angle measuring $60°$, then it is not equiangular; true
c. $a + b = 135$
d. $a = 54$
e. **(1)** $\angle 3 \cong \angle 4$ (Given)
(2) Either $KL = JK$ or $KL \neq JK$. Assume $KL = JK$. (A statement is either true or false.)
(3) $\angle 4 \cong \angle J$ (Base Angles Theorem)
(4) $\angle 3 \cong \angle J$ (Transitive or Substitution)
(5) $KL \neq JK$ (Statement 4 contradicts the Exterior Angle Inequality Theorem. The assumption made in statement 2 must be false. By elimination,

statement 5 must be true.)

Problem Set 48
1. True
2. True
3. If not a, then not b
4. If not b, then not a
5. complementary
6. $a > b$; Multiplication Property of Inequality
7. Greater than 3 and less than 5
8. Greater than 10 and less than 28
9. Inverse
10. Converse
11. Contrapositive
12. Converse: If Jane lives in California, then she lives in Los Angeles; false
Inverse: If Jane does not live in Los Angeles, then she does not live in California; false
Contrapositive: If Jane does not live in California, then she does not live in Los Angeles; true
13. Converse: If two angles are supplementary, then they are a linear pair; false.
Inverse: If two angles are not a linear pair, then they are not supplementary; false.
Contrapositive: If two angles are not supplementary, then

they are not a linear pair; true.

14. 30°, 55°, 95°; obtuse
15. 15°, 75°, 90°
16. If two parallel lines are cut by a transversal, then alternate exterior angles are congruent.
17. If two parallel lines are cut by a transversal, then corresponding angles are congruent.
18. If two lines form supplementary interior angles on the same side of a transversal, then the lines are parallel.
19. $w + x + y + z = 300$
20. $s + t = 130$
21. $x = 100 - y$
22. $b = 40$
23. **(1)** G is between H and E (Given)
(2) $m\angle HGD > m\angle GED$ (Exterior Angle Inequality Theorem)
(3) $m\angle GED > m\angle F$ (Exterior Angle Inequality Theorem)
(4) $m\angle HGD > m\angle F$ (Transitive)
24. **(1)** $\angle 1 \cong \angle 2$ (Given)
(2) Either $RS = ST$ or $RS \neq ST$. Assume $RS = ST$. (A statement is either true or false.)
(3) $\angle 2 \cong \angle T$ (Base Angles Theorem)
(4) $\angle 1 \cong \angle T$ (Transitive or Substitution)
(5) $RS \neq ST$ (Statement 4 contradicts the Exterior Angle Inequality Theorem. The assumption made in statement 2 must be false. By elimination, statement 5 must be true.)

Practice 49

a. Inverse
b. Converse: If a figure is a square, then it is a polygon; true
Inverse: If a figure is not a polygon, then it is not a square; true
Contrapositive: If a figure is not a square, then it is not a polygon; false
c. $\overline{JQ}$
d. If Unequal Angles, then Unequal Sides
e. **(1)** $KN = PN$ (Given)
(2) Either $PM = MO$ or $PM \neq MO$. Assume $PM = MO$. (A statement is either true or false.)
(3) $m\angle 3 = m\angle 4$ (Base Angles Theorem)
(4) $m\angle 4 > m\angle K$ (Exterior Angle Inequality Theorem)
(5) $m\angle 3 > m\angle K$ (Substitution)
(6) $m\angle NPK > m\angle 3$ (Whole Greater than Its Part)
(7) $m\angle NPK > m\angle K$ (Transitive)
(8) $KN > PN$ (If Unequal Angles, then Unequal Sides)
(9) $PM \neq MO$ (Statement 8 contradicts the given statement that $KN = PN$. The assumption made in statement 2 must be false. By elimination, statement 9 must be true.)

Problem Set 49

1. True
2. True
3. Vertical angles
4. If b, then a
5. altitude
6. always
7. never
8. Converse
9. Inverse
10. Converse: If James lives in Miami, then he lives in Florida; true
Inverse: If James does not live in Florida, then he does not live in Miami; true
Contrapositive: If James does not live in Miami, then he does not live in Florida; false
11. Converse: If a figure is a triangle, then it is a polygon; true

Inverse: If a figure is not a polygon, then it is not a triangle; true
Contrapositive: If a figure is not a triangle, then it is not a polygon; false

12. $\angle A$
13. $\overline{DF}$
14. C.P.C.T.C.
15. If Unequal Sides, then Unequal Angles
16. If Unequal Angles, then Unequal Sides
17. Angle-Angle-Side or Angle-Side-Angle
18. Side-Angle-Side
19. $p + q = 146$
20. $m\angle NRT = 109$
21. $c = 180 - 3a$
22. $x = 34$
23. **(1)** $m\angle 5 = m\angle 6$ (Given)
    (2) $m\angle 5 > m\angle C$ (Exterior Angle Inequality Theorem)
    (3) $m\angle 6 > m\angle C$ (Substitution)
    (4) $EC > AE$ (If Unequal Angles, then Unequal Sides)
24. **(1)** $AB = CB$ (Given)
    (2) Either $AD = DE$ or $AD \neq DE$. Assume $AD = DE$. (A statement is either true or false.)
    (3) $m\angle 1 = m\angle 2$ (Base Angles Theorem)
    (4) $m\angle 2 > m\angle C$ (Exterior Angle Inequality Theorem)
    (5) $m\angle 1 > m\angle C$ (Substitution)

(6) $m\angle BAC > m\angle 1$ (Whole Greater than Its Part)
(7) $m\angle BAC > m\angle C$ (Transitive)
(8) $AB < CB$ (If Unequal Angles, then Unequal Sides)
(9) $AD \neq DE$ (Statement 8 contradicts the given statement that $AB = CB$. The assumption made in statement 2 must be false. By elimination, statement 9 must be true.)

CHAPTER 8

Practice 50

a. Consecutive sides: $\overline{ST}$ and $\overline{TQ}$, $\overline{TQ}$ and $\overline{QW}$, $\overline{QW}$ and $\overline{SW}$, $\overline{SW}$ and $\overline{ST}$
Opposite sides: $\overline{ST}$ and $\overline{QW}$, $\overline{TQ}$ and $\overline{SW}$

b. Converse: If an angle has a measure of greater than 90° (and less than 180°), then it is obtuse; true
Inverse: If an angle is not obtuse, then it does not have a measure of greater than 90° (and less than 180°); true
Contrapositive: If an angle does not have a measure of greater than 90° (and less than 180°), then it is not obtuse; true

c. $\angle J$

d. $x = 73$

e. (1) $\triangle ABC$ is equilateral; Point Q is any point on $\overline{AB}$. (Given)
(2) $m\angle CQA > m\angle B$ (Exterior Angle Inequality Theorem)
(3) $m\angle A = m\angle B$ (If a triangle is equilateral, then it is equiangular.)
(4) $m\angle CQA > m\angle A$ (Substitution)

(5) $CQ < AC$ (If Unequal Angles, then Unequal Sides)
(6) $AC = CB = AB$ (Definition of equilateral triangle)
(7) $CQ < BC$ and $CQ < AB$ (Substitution)

Problem Set 50

1. True
2. False
3. Consecutive
4. Opposite
5. inverse
6. not congruent; greater; longer
7. Consecutive sides: $\overline{LK}$ and $\overline{KI}$, $\overline{KI}$ and $\overline{IO}$, $\overline{IO}$ and $\overline{LO}$, $\overline{LO}$ and $\overline{LK}$
Opposite sides: $\overline{LK}$ and $\overline{IO}$, $\overline{KI}$ and $\overline{LO}$
8. Consecutive angles: $\angle L$ and $\angle K$, $\angle K$ and $\angle I$, $\angle I$ and $\angle O$, $\angle O$ and $\angle L$
Opposite angles: $\angle L$ and $\angle I$, $\angle K$ and $\angle O$
9. Greater than 9 and less than 19
10. Greater than 20 and less than 110
11. Contrapositive
12. Inverse
13. Converse: If an angle has a measure of less than 90°, then it is acute; true
Inverse: If an angle is not acute, then it does

not have a measure of less than 90°; true
Contrapositive: If an angle does not have a measure of less than 90°, then it is not acute; true

14. Converse: If two angles are complementary, then they are the acute angles of a right triangle; false
Inverse: If two angles are not the acute angles of a right triangle, then they are not complementary; false
Contrapositive: If two angles are not complementary, then they are not the acute angles of a right triangle; true

15. $\overline{BC}$
16. $\angle R$
17. Exterior Angle of a Triangle Theorem
18. If Unequal Sides, then Unequal Angles
19. $x = 70$
20. $y = 76$
21. $m\angle B = 40$, $m\angle C = 20$
22. 135°, 45°
23. (1) $EU = UT$ (Given)
(2) $m\angle 1 = m\angle 2$ (Base Angles Theorem)
(3) $m\angle 3 > m\angle 2$ (Exterior Angle Inequality Theorem)

(4) $m\angle 3 > m\angle 1$ (Substitution)
(5) $EU > UR$ (If Unequal Angles, then Unequal Sides)

24. **(1)** $\triangle JKL$ is equilateral; Point P is any point on $\overline{JL}$. (Given)
(2) $m\angle KPJ > m\angle L$ (Exterior Angle Inequality Theorem)
(3) $m\angle J = m\angle L$ (If a triangle is equilateral, then it is equiangular.)
(4) $m\angle KPJ > m\angle J$ (Substitution)
(5) $KP < JK$ (If Unequal Angles, then Unequal Sides)
(6) $JK = KL = JL$ (Definition of equilateral triangle)
(7) $KP < KL$ and $KP < JL$ (Substitution)

Practice 51

a. Trapezoid
b.

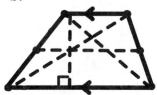

c. Converse: If two lines do not intersect to form right angles, then they are not perpendicular; true
Inverse: If two lines are perpendicular, then they intersect to form right angles; true
Contrapositive: If two lines intersect to form right angles, then they are perpendicular; true
d. $y = 75$
e. **(1)** Trapezoid $ABCD$, $AL = MD$ (Given)
(2) $AL + LM = MD + LM$ (Addition Property)
(3) $AM = AL + LM$ and $DL = MD + LM$ (Betweenness of Points)
(4) $AM = DL$ (Substitution)
(5) $KL = KM$ (Given)
(6) $m\angle KLM = m\angle KML$ (Base Angles Theorem)
(7) $BM = CL$ (Given)
(8) $\triangle BAM \cong \triangle CDL$ (S.A.S.)
(9) $BA = CD$ (C.P.C.T.C.)
(10) Trapezoid $ABCD$ is isosceles. (Definition of isosceles trapezoid)

Problem Set 51

1. False
2. True
3. bases
4. congruent
5. contrapositive
6. Isosceles trapezoid
7. trapezoid
8. quadrilateral

9.

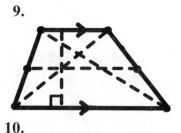

10.

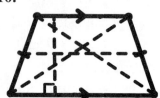

11. Converse: If a triangle is not equiangular, then it is not equilateral; true
Inverse: If a triangle is equilateral, then it is equiangular; true
Contrapositive: If a triangle is equiangular, then it is equilateral; true
12. Converse: If a polygon is a quadrilateral, then it has four sides; true
Inverse: If a polygon does not have four sides, then it is not a quadrilateral; true
Contrapositive: If a polygon is not a quadrilateral, then it does not have four sides; true
13. $\angle R$
14. $\overline{AC}$
15. $\angle F$
16. If two angles are supplementary to congruent angles,

then they are congruent.

17. Definition of trapezoid

18. The diagonals of an isosceles trapezoid are congruent.

19. $y = 40$

20. $z = 36$

21. $x = 80$

22. $SH = 7$

23. (1) $\triangle ABC$ is not isosceles (Given)
    (2) Either $\triangle APC$ is not isosceles or $\triangle APC$ is isosceles. Assume $\triangle APC$ is isosceles. (A statement is either true or false.)
    (3) $AP = PC$ (Definition of isosceles triangle)
    (4) $\angle 1 \cong \angle 2$ (Given)
    (5) $PB = PB$ (Reflexive)
    (6) $\triangle BPA \cong \triangle BPC$ (S.A.S.)
    (7) $AB = BC$ (C.P.C.T.C.)
    (8) $\triangle ABC$ is isosceles (Definition of isosceles triangle)
    (9) $\triangle APC$ is not isosceles (Statement 8 contradicts the given statement that $\triangle ABC$ is not isosceles. The assumption made in statement 2 must be false. By elimination, statement 9 must be true.)

24. (1) Trapezoid $RSTU$, $RP = UQ$ (Given)
    (2) $RP + PQ = UQ + PQ$ (Addition Property)
    (3) $RQ = RP + PQ$ and $UP = UQ + PQ$ (Betweenness of Points)
    (4) $RQ = UP$ (Substitution)
    (5) $VP = VQ$ (Given)
    (6) $m\angle VPQ = m\angle VQP$ (Base Angles Theorem)
    (7) $SQ = TP$ (Given)
    (8) $\triangle SRQ \cong \triangle TUP$ (S.A.S.)
    (9) $SR = TU$ (C.P.C.T.C.)
    (10) Trapezoid $RSTU$ is isosceles. (Definition of isosceles trapezoid)

Practice 52

a. $\overline{RW}$

b. $\overline{DE}$

c. Pairs of opposite angles of a parallelogram are congruent.

d. $x = 14$

e. (1) Parallelogram $MNOP$, $MP > OP$ (Given)
   (2) $m\angle MOP > m\angle OMP$ (If Unequal Sides, then Unequal Angles)
   (3) $\overline{NM} \parallel \overline{OP}$ (Definition of parallelogram)
   (4) $m\angle NMO = m\angle MOP$ (If two parallel lines are cut by a transversal, then their alternate interior angles are equal.)
   (5) $m\angle NMO > m\angle OMP$ (Substitution)

Problem Set 52

1. True
2. False
3. base angles
4. Consecutive
5. 360
6. Consecutive sides: $\overline{DP}$ and $\overline{PR}$, $\overline{PR}$ and $\overline{RT}$, $\overline{RT}$ and $\overline{DT}$, $\overline{DT}$ and $\overline{DP}$ Opposite sides: $\overline{DP}$ and $\overline{RT}$, $\overline{PR}$ and $\overline{DT}$
7. Consecutive angles: $\angle D$ and $\angle P$, $\angle P$ and $\angle R$, $\angle R$ and $\angle T$, $\angle T$ and $\angle D$ Opposite angles: $\angle D$ and $\angle R$, $\angle P$ and $\angle T$
8. always
9. sometimes
10. Inverse
11. Converse
12. $\overline{JF}$
13. $\angle B$
14. $\overline{BC}$
15. Hypotenuse-Leg
16. Pairs of opposite angles of a paral-

lelogram are congruent.

17. $42°$, $69°$, $69°$
18. $45°$, $60°$, $75°$; acute triangle
19. $z = 130$
20. $e = 111$
21. $y = 42$
22. $x = 18$
23. **(1)** $ABCD$ and $AFGH$ are parallelograms (Given)
   (2) $\angle G \cong \angle A$ and $\angle A \cong \angle C$ (Pairs of opposite angles of a parallelogram are congruent.)
   (3) $\angle G \cong \angle C$ (Transitive or Substitution)
24. **(1)** Given: Parallelogram $DFGJ$, $DJ > DF$ (Given)
   (2) $m\angle DFJ > m\angle DJF$ (If Unequal Sides, then Unequal Angles)
   (3) $\overline{FD} \parallel \overline{GJ}$ (Definition of parallelogram)
   (4) $m\angle GJF = m\angle DFJ$ (If two parallel lines are cut by a transversal, then their alternate interior angles are equal.)
   (5) $m\angle GJF > m\angle DJF$ (Substitution)

Practice 53

a. $\overline{CD}$
b. 6.5

c. If a quadrilateral is a parallelogram, then the diagonals bisect each other.
d. $y = 1$
e. **(1)** Parallelogram $DEFG$, (Given)
   (2) $\overline{DE} \cong \overline{GF}$ (If a quadrilateral is a parallelogram, then both pairs of opposite sides are congruent.)
   (3) $\overline{DE} \parallel \overline{GF}$ (Definition of parallelogram)
   (4) $\angle EDH \cong \angle GFI$ (If two parallel lines are cut by a transversal, their alternate interior angles are congruent.)
   (5) $\overline{DH} \cong \overline{FI}$ (Given)
   (6) $\triangle DEH \cong \triangle FGI$ (S.A.S.)
   (7) $\angle DEH \cong \angle FGI$ (C.P.C.T.C.)

Problem Set 53

1. True
2. True
3. trapezoid
4. parallelogram
5. congruent
6. Trapezoid
7. Quadrilateral
8. Parallelogram
9. Isosceles trapezoid
10. Converse: If a figure is a quadrilateral, then it is a parallelogram; false
   Inverse: If a figure is not a parallelogram,

then it is not a quadrilateral; false
   Contrapositive: If a figure is not a quadrilateral, then it is not a parallelogram; true
11. Converse: If a figure is not a trapezoid, then it is a not a quadrilateral; false
   Inverse: If a figure is a quadrilateral, then it is a trapezoid; false
   Contrapositive: If a figure is a trapezoid, then it is a quadrilateral; true
12. $\overline{BP}$
13. $\overline{PT}$
14. 5.5
15. If a quadrilateral is a parallelogram, then both pairs of opposite sides are congruent.
16. If a quadrilateral is a parallelogram, then the diagonals bisect each other.
17. $p + q = 70$
18. $x = 48$
19. $y = 10$
20. $x = 16$
21. $m\angle E = 75$, $m\angle F = 25$
22. $62°$, $28°$
23. **(1)** $\overline{BM}$ is an altitude of $\triangle ABC$. (Given)
   (2) $\angle AMB$ and $\angle CMB$ are right angles (Perpendicular lines intersect to form right angles.)
   (3) $\triangle AMB$ and $\triangle CMB$ are right

triangles (Definition of right triangle)

(4) $\overline{AB} \cong \overline{BC}$ (Given)

(5) $\overline{BM} \cong \overline{BM}$ (Reflexive)

(6) $\triangle AMB \cong \triangle CMB$ (Hypotenuse-Leg)

(7) $\overline{AM} \cong \overline{MC}$ (C.P.C.T.C.)

(8) Point M is the midpoint of $\overline{AC}$. (Definition of midpoint)

24. (1) Parallelogram $SPQT$, (Given)

(2) $\overline{PS} \cong \overline{QT}$ (If a quadrilateral is a parallelogram, then both pairs of opposite sides are congruent.)

(3) $\overline{PS} \parallel \overline{QT}$ (Definition of parallelogram)

(4) $\angle SPK \cong \angle QTL$ (If two parallel lines are cut by a transversal, their alternate interior angles are congruent.)

(5) $\overline{PK} \cong \overline{TL}$ (Given)

(6) $\triangle PSK \cong \triangle TQL$ (S.A.S.)

(7) $\angle PSK \cong \angle TQL$ (C.P.C.T.C.)

Practice 54

a. Parallelogram
b. Parallelogram
c. If both pairs of opposite sides are congruent, then a quadrilateral is a parallelogram.

d. $m\angle EKD = 85$

e. (1) Isosceles trapezoid $MNPQ$, $\angle QSP \cong \angle QPS$ (Given)

(2) $\angle MNS \cong \angle QPS$ (The upper base angles of an isosceles trapezoid are congruent.)

(3) $\angle MNS \cong \angle QSP$ (Transitive or Substitution)

(4) $\overline{MN} \parallel \overline{SQ}$ (If two lines form congruent corresponding angles with a transversal, then the lines are parallel.)

(5) $\overline{MQ} \parallel \overline{NS}$ (Definition of isosceles trapezoid)

(6) $MNSP$ is a parallelogram. (Definition of parallelogram)

Problem Set 54

1. True
2. True
3. consecutive
4. diagonals
5. 360
6. Trapezoid
7. Parallelogram
8. Isosceles trapezoid
9. Parallelogram
10. sometimes
11. never
12. Contrapositive
13. Converse
14. $\overline{HJ}$
15. $\angle A$

16. If both pairs of opposite sides are congruent, then a quadrilateral is a parallelogram (definition of parallelogram).

17. If both pairs of opposite angles are congruent, then the quadrilateral is a parallelogram.

18. If a quadrilateral is a parallelogram, then the diagonals bisect each other.

19. $a + b = 180$
20. $y = 144$
21. $x = 5$
22. $m\angle TQR = 80$

23. (1) Isosceles trapezoid $PQST$ (Given)

(2) $\overline{QP} \cong \overline{ST}$ (Definition of isosceles trapezoid)

(3) $\angle PQS \cong \angle TSQ$ (The upper base angles of an isosceles trapezoid are congruent.)

(4) $\overline{QS} \cong \overline{QS}$ (Reflexive Property)

(5) $\triangle PQS \cong \triangle TSQ$ (S.A.S.)

(6) $\angle QSU \cong \angle TQS$ (C.P.C.T.C)

(7) $\overline{QU} \cong \overline{US}$ (Converse Base Angles Theorem)

(8) $\triangle QSU$ is isosceles. (Definition of isosceles triangle)

24. **(1)** Isosceles trapezoid *EFGH*, $\angle FEJ \cong \angle FJE$ (Given)
(2) $\angle FEJ \cong \angle GHJ$ (The lower base angles of an isosceles trapezoid are congruent.)
(3) $\angle FJE \cong \angle GHJ$ (Transitive or Substitution)
(4) $\overline{FJ} \parallel \overline{GH}$ (If two lines form congruent corresponding angles with a transversal, then the lines are parallel.)
(5) $\overline{FG} \parallel \overline{JH}$ (Definition of isosceles trapezoid)
(6) *FJGH* is a parallelogram. (Definition of parallelogram)

Practice 55

a. If one pair of opposite sides are both parallel and congruent, then a quadrilateral is a parallelogram.
b. $p = 65$, $q = 115$, $r = 115$, $s = 65$
c. $x = 5$, $y = 7$
d. $155°$, $25°$
e. **(1)** $\triangle KJL \cong \triangle MNL$ (Given)
(2) $\overline{KJ} \cong \overline{MN}$ (C.P.C.T.C.)
(3) *N* is the midpoint of $\overline{MO}$. (Given)

(4) $\overline{MN} \cong \overline{NO}$ (Definition of midpoint)
(5) $\overline{KJ} \cong \overline{NO}$ (Transitive or substitution)
(6) $\angle M \cong \angle KJL$ (C.P.C.T.C.)
(7) $\overline{KJ} \parallel \overline{NO}$ (If two lines form congruent alternate interior angles, then the lines are parallel.)
(8) *KJON* is a parallelogram. (If one pair of opposite sides is both parallel and congruent, then a quadrilateral is a parallelogram.)

Problem Set 55

1. False
2. False
3. opposite
4. opposite
5. trapezoid
6. bases
7. Converse: If a figure is a quadrilateral, then it is a polygon; true
Inverse: If a figure is not a polygon, then it is not a quadrilateral; true
Contrapositive: If a figure is not a quadrilateral, then it is not a polygon; false
8. Converse: If a figure is not a polygon, then it is not a parallelogram; true

Inverse: If a figure is a parallelogram, then it is a polygon; true
Contrapositive: If a figure is a polygon, then it is a parallelogram; false
9. $\angle C$
10. $\angle K$
11. $\overline{WR}$
12. Side-Side-Side
13. Angle-Angle-Side
14. If one pair of opposite sides are both parallel and congruent, then a quadrilateral is a parallelogram.
15. If the diagonals bisect each other, then the quadrilateral is a parallelogram.
16. Side-Side-Side
17. $x = 51$
18. $u = 70$, $x = 110$, $y = 110$, $z = 70$
19. $x = 82$, $y = 98$, $z = 98$
20. $x = 4$, $y = 6$
21. $34°$, $56°$
22. $125°$, $55°$
23. **(1)** $\triangle BCD \cong \triangle EFD$ (Given)
(2) $\overline{BC} \cong \overline{EF}$ (C.P.C.T.C.)
(3) *B* is the midpoint of $\overline{AC}$ (Given)
(4) $\overline{AB} \cong \overline{BC}$ (Definition of midpoint)
(5) $\overline{AB} \cong \overline{EF}$ (Transitive or substitution)
(6) $\angle C \cong \angle DFE$ (C.P.C.T.C.)

(7) $\overline{AB} \parallel \overline{EF}$ (If two lines form congruent alternate interior angles, then the lines are parallel.)

(8) *ABEF* is a parallelogram. (If one pair of opposite sides is both parallel and congruent, then a quadrilateral is a parallelogram.)

24. **(4)** Definition of midpoint
     (5) Pairs of vertical angles are congruent.
     (6) S.A.S.
     (9) Transitive or Substitution
     (10) C.P.C.T.C.
     (12) If one pair of opposite sides are both parallel and congruent, then the quadrilateral is a parallelogram.
     (13) If a quadrilateral is a parallelogram, then both pairs of opposite sides are parallel (and congruent).

Practice 56

a. Rhombus
b. Parallelogram
c. $b = a + c$
d. $y = 4$
e. **(1)** *ABCD* is a rhombus. (Given)
    (2) $\overline{AB} \cong \overline{BC}$ $\cong \overline{CD} \cong \overline{AD}$

(Definition of rhombus)

(3) $\overline{BE} \cong \overline{CF}$, $\overline{CE} \cong \overline{FD}$ (Given)

(4) $\triangle CBE \cong \triangle DCF$ (S.S.S.)

(5) $\angle B \cong \angle DCF$ (C.P.C.T.C.)

(6) $\overline{AB} \parallel \overline{CD}$ (Definition of parallelogram)

(7) $m\angle B + m\angle DCF = 180$ (If two parallel lines are cut by a transversal, interior angles on the same side of the transversal are supplementary.)

(8) $m\angle B + m\angle B = 180$ or $2m\angle B = 180$, (Substitution)

(9) $m\angle B = 90$ (Division)

(10) $m\angle DCF = 90$, (Substitution)

(11) $m\angle A = 90$, $m\angle ADC = 90$ (Pairs of opposite angles in a rhombus/parallelogram are equal.)

(12) *ABCD* is a square. (Definition of square)

Problem Set 56

1. True
2. True
3. parallel; one-half
4. bisect each other
5. square
6. Isosceles trapezoid
7. Rectangle
8. Rhombus
9. Parallelogram

10. always
11. never
12. sometimes
13. Converse
14. Inverse
15. 20°, 40°, 120°
16. 30°, 60°, 90°
17. $\angle D$
18. $\overline{AB}$
19. $b = 5$
20. $y = x + z$
21. $g = 30$
22. $x = 3$
23. **(1)** Rectangle *DEFG* (Given)
     (2) $\angle E$ and $\angle F$ are right angles. (Definition of rectangle)
     (3) $\angle E \cong \angle F$ (All right angles are congruent.)
     (4) *T* is the midpoint of $\overline{EF}$. (Given)
     (5) $\overline{ET} \cong \overline{TF}$ (Definition of midpoint)
     (6) $\overline{ED} \cong \overline{FG}$ (If a quadrilateral is a rectangle/parallelogram, then both pairs of opposite sides are congruent.)
     (7) $\triangle DET \cong \triangle GFT$ (S.A.S.)
     (8) $\overline{DT} \cong \overline{GT}$ (C.P.C.T.C.)
     (9) $\triangle DTG$ is isosceles. (Definition of isosceles)
24. **(1)** *JKLM* is a rhombus. (Given)
     (2) $\overline{JK} \cong \overline{KL}$ $\cong \overline{LM} \cong \overline{JM}$

(Definition of rhombus)

(3) $\overline{KP} \cong \overline{JQ}$, $\overline{LP} \cong \overline{KQ}$ (Given)

(4) $\triangle KJQ \cong \triangle LKP$ (S.S.S.)

(5) $\angle LKP \cong \angle J$ (C.P.C.T.C.)

(6) $\overline{KL} \parallel \overline{JM}$ (Definition of parallelogram)

(7) $m\angle LKP + m\angle J = 180$ (If two parallel lines are cut by a transversal, then interior angles on the same side of the transversal are supplementary.)

(8) $m\angle J + m\angle J = 180$ or $2m\angle J = 180$ (Substitution)

(9) $m\angle J = 90$ (Division)

(10) $m\angle LKP = 90$, (Substitution)

(11) $m\angle M = 90$, $m\angle KLM = 90$ (Pairs of opposite angles in a rhombus/parallelogram are equal.)

(12) $JKLM$ is a square. (Definition of square)

Practice 57

a. Converse: If a figure is a rectangle, then it is a square; false
Inverse: If a figure is not a square, then it is not a rectangle; false

Contrapositive: If a figure is not a rectangle, then it is not a square; true

b. The diagonals of a rhombus are perpendicular to each other.

c. $a = 9$, $b = 126$, $c = 126$

d. $m\angle ADC = 95$

e. **(1)** Rhombus $LKJN$ (Given)

(2) $\overline{KN} \cong \overline{LJ}$, $\overline{LK} \cong \overline{JN}$ (Definition of rhombus)

(3) $\angle L \cong \angle N$ (Both pairs of opposite angles of a rhombus/parallelogram are congruent.)

(4) $\triangle KNJ \cong \triangle KLJ$ (S.A.S.)

(5) $\angle 1 \cong \angle 2$, $\angle 3 \cong \angle 4$ (C.P.C.T.C.)

Problem Set 57

1. False
2. True
3. rectangle
4. rhombus
5. trapezoid
6. opposite
7. Rhombus
8. Quadrilateral
9. Square
10. Converse: If a figure is not a rectangle, then it is not a parallelogram; false
Inverse: If a figure is a parallelogram, then it is a rectangle; false
Contrapositive: If a figure is a rectangle,

then it is a parallelogram; true

11. Converse: If a figure is a rhombus, then it is a square; false
Inverse: If a figure is not a square, then it is not a rhombus; false
Contrapositive: If a figure is not a rhombus, then it is not a square; true

12. 8.5
13. $\angle A$
14. The diagonals of a rectangle are congruent.
15. The diagonals of a rhombus are perpendicular to each other.
16. Base Angles Theorem
17. $x = 50$
18. $m\angle S = 68$, $m\angle D = 112$
19. $x = 15$, $y = 105$, $z = 105$
20. $m\angle DPI = 116$
21. $m\angle A = 80$, $m\angle B = 40$
22. $50°$, $40°$
23. **(1)** Rectangle $ATPZ$ (Given)

(2) $\overline{AT} \cong \overline{ZP}$ (Both pairs of opposite sides of a rectangle/parallelogram are congruent.)

(3) $\angle T \cong \angle Z$ (Both pairs of opposite angles of a rectangle/parallelogram are congruent.)

(4) $\overline{TV} \cong \overline{BZ}$ (Given)

(5) $\Delta TAV \cong \Delta ZPB$
(S.A.S.)
(6) $\overline{AV} \cong \overline{PB}$
(C.P.C.T.C.)

24. **(1)** Rhombus $ABCD$
(Given)
(2) $\overline{AD} \cong \overline{CB}$,
$\overline{AB} \cong \overline{DC}$ (Definition of rhombus)
(3) $\angle D \cong \angle B$ (Both pairs of opposite angles of a rhombus/parallelogram are congruent.)
(4) $\Delta ADC \cong \Delta ABC$
(S.A.S.)
(5) $\angle 1 \cong \angle 2$,
$\angle 3 \cong \angle 4$
(C.P.C.T.C.)

CHAPTER 9

Practice 58

a. Pentagon; concave
b. 9 diagonals

c. $x = 4$, $y = 3$
d. $a + b + c = 360$
e. **(1)** Parallelogram *AECF*. (Given)
(2) $\overline{AE} \parallel \overline{FC}$ (Definition of parallelogram)
(3) $\angle AEF \cong \angle CFE$ (If two parallel lines are cut by a transversal, then alternate interior angles are congruent.)
(4) $\angle AEF$ and $\angle AEB$ are supplementary. $\angle CFE$ and $\angle CFD$ are supplementary. (If two angles are a linear pair, then they are supplementary.)
(5) $\angle AEB \cong \angle CFD$ (If two angles are supplementary to congruent angles, then they are congruent.)
(6) $\overline{BE} \cong \overline{DF}$ (Given)
(7) $\overline{AE} \cong \overline{FC}$ (If a quadrilateral is a parallelogram, then

both pairs of opposite sides are congruent)
(8) $\triangle AEB \cong \triangle CFD$ (S.A.S.)
(9) $\overline{AB} \cong \overline{CD}$ (C.P.C.T.C.)
(10) $\angle ABE \cong \angle CDF$ (C.P.C.T.C.)
(11) $\overline{AB} \parallel \overline{CD}$ (If two lines form congruent alternate interior angles with a transversal, then the lines are parallel.)
(12) *ABCD* is a parallelogram. (If one pair of opposite sides is both parallel and congruent, then a quadrilateral is a parallelogram.)

Problem Set 58

1. False
2. True
3. pentagon, hexagon
4. diagonals
5. square
6. Heptagon; convex
7. Hexagon; concave
8. Octagon; convex
9. 5 diagonals

10. 2 diagonals

11. sometimes

12. always
13. Contrapositive
14. Inverse
15. $\angle K$
16. $\overline{LW}$
17. If both pairs of opposite sides are congruent, then a quadrilateral is a parallelogram.
18. If a quadrilateral is a parallelogram, then both pairs of opposite angles are congruent.
19. $x = 12$
20. $x = 5$, $y = 6$
21. $p = 23$, $q = 18$
22. $r + s + t = 360$
23. **(1)** Rhombus *TCBV*, $\overline{CU} \perp \overline{BV}$, $\overline{CS} \perp \overline{TV}$ (Given)
(2) $\angle CST$ and $\angle CUB$ are right angles (Perpendicular lines intersect to form right angles.)
(3) $\angle CST \cong \angle CUB$ (All right angles are congruent.)
(4) $\overline{CB} \cong \overline{CT}$ (Definition of rhombus)
(5) $\angle T \cong \angle B$ (If a quadrilateral is a rhombus/parallelogram, then both pairs of opposite angles are congruent.)
(6) $\triangle CTS \cong \triangle CBU$ (A.A.S.)
(7) $\overline{CU} \cong \overline{CS}$ (C.P.C.T.C.)

24. (1) Parallelogram *RJTI*. (Given)
(2) $\overline{RI} \parallel \overline{JT}$ (Definition of parallelogram)
(3) $\angle RIJ \cong \angle TJI$ (If two parallel lines are cut by a transversal, then alternate interior angles are congruent.)
(4) $\angle RIJ$ and $\angle RIE$ are supplementary. $\angle TJI$ and $\angle TJS$ are supplementary. (If two angles are a linear pair, then they are supplementary.)
(5) $\angle RIE \cong \angle TJS$ (If two angles are supplementary to congruent angles, then they are congruent.)
(6) $\overline{EI} \cong \overline{SJ}$ (Given)
(7) $\overline{RI} \cong \overline{JT}$ (If a quadrilateral is a parallelogram, then both pairs of opposite sides are congruent)
(8) $\triangle RIE \cong \triangle TJS$ (S.A.S.)
(9) $\overline{RE} \cong \overline{ST}$ (C.P.C.T.C.)
(10) $\angle REI \cong \angle TSJ$ (C.P.C.T.C.)
(11) $\overline{RE} \parallel \overline{ST}$ (If two lines form congruent alternate interior angles with a transversal, then the lines are parallel.)
(12) *ERST* is a parallelogram. (If one pair of opposite sides is both parallel and congruent, then a quadrilateral is a parallelogram.)

Practice 59

a. 540°
b. The diagonals of a rhombus bisect the angles at the vertices which they join.
c. $y = 88$
d. 100°, 80°
e. (1) Quadrilateral *FGHI*, $\overline{GF} \parallel \overline{HK}$, and $\overline{GF} \cong \overline{HK}$ (Given)
(2) *GHKF* is a parallelogram (If one pair of opposite sides is both parallel and congruent, then the quadrilateral is a parallelogram.)
(3) $\overline{GH} \parallel \overline{FK}$ and $\overline{GH} \parallel \overline{FI}$ (Definition of parallelogram)
(4) *FGHI* is a trapezoid. (Definition of trapezoid)

Problem Set 59

1. True
2. False
3. heptagon, decagon
4. consecutive
5. legs
6. Rectangle
7. Rhombus
8. Trapezoid
9. 720°
10. 900°
11. 360°
12. Converse: If a figure is a polygon, then it is a nonagon; false
Inverse: If a figure is not a nonagon, then it is not a polygon; false
Contrapositive: If a figure is not a polygon, then it is not a nonagon; true
13. Converse: If a figure has four congruent sides, then it is a square; false
Inverse: If a figure is not a square, then it does not have four congruent sides; false
Contrapositive: If a figure does not have four congruent sides, then it is not a square; true
14. 94°, 43°, 43°
15. 45°, 63°, 72°
16. A rhombus is a parallelogram with four congruent sides. (Definition of rhombus)
17. The diagonals of a rhombus bisect the angles at the vertices which they join.
18. $m\overline{TU} = 5$
19. $x + y + z = 270$
20. $x = 130$
21. 75°, 15°
22. 105°, 75°
23. (1) $\angle B \cong \angle D$ and $\angle A \cong \angle C$ (Given)

(2) *ABCD* is a parallelogram (If both pairs of opposite angles are congruent, then a quadrilateral is a parallelogram.)

(3) $\overline{AB} \cong \overline{DC}$ (If a quadrilateral is a parallelogram, then both pairs of opposite sides are congruent.)

24. **(1)** Quadrilateral *LPRS*, $\overline{PT} \parallel \overline{RS}$, and $\overline{PT} \cong \overline{RS}$ (Given)

(2) *PRST* is a parallelogram (If one pair of opposite sides is both parallel and congruent, then the quadrilateral is a parallelogram.)

(3) $\overline{PR} \parallel \overline{TS}$ and $\overline{PR} \parallel \overline{LS}$ (Definition of parallelogram)

(4) *LPRS* is a trapezoid. (Definition of trapezoid)

Practice 60

a. 360°

b. If Unequal Angles, then Unequal Sides

c. $a + b = 90 + c$

d. $MP = 9$

e. **(1)** Rectangle *ABCD*, $\overline{BP} \cong \overline{CP}$ (Given)

(2) $\angle PBC \cong \angle PCB$ (Base Angles Theorem)

(3) $\overline{BC} \parallel \overline{AD}$ (Definition of rectangle-/parallelogram)

(4) $\angle BLA \cong \angle PBC$, $\angle CMD \cong \angle PCB$ (If two parallel lines are cut by a transversal, then alternate interior angles are congruent.)

(5) $\angle CMD \cong \angle PBC$ (Transitive)

(6) $\angle BLA \cong \angle CMD$ (Transitive)

(7) $\angle A$ and $\angle D$ are right angles (Definition of rectangle)

(8) $\angle A \cong \angle D$ (All right angles are congruent.)

(9) $\overline{AB} \cong \overline{CD}$ (If a quadrilateral is a rectangle/parallelogram, then both pairs of opposite sides are congruent.)

(10) $\triangle BLA \cong \triangle CMD$ (A.A.S.)

(11) $\overline{AL} \cong \overline{DM}$ (C.P.C.T.C.)

Problem Set 60

1. False
2. True
3. quadrilateral; nonagon
4. congruent
5. Base Angles Theorem
6. Pentagon
7. Decagon
8. 1,080°
9. 540°
10. 360°
11. 360°
12. never
13. never
14. Converse
15. Inverse
16. 20.5
17. $\angle F$
18. If a quadrilateral is a parallelogram, then the diagonals bisect each other.
19. If Unequal Angles, then Unequal Sides
20. $r + s = 120$
21. $x + y = 90 + z$
22. $EA = 7$
23. **(1)** *HIJK* is a rectangle. (Given)

(2) $\overline{IK} \cong \overline{HJ}$ (The diagonals of a rectangle are congruent.)

(3) *HIKL* is a parallelogram. (Given)

(4) $\overline{IK} \cong \overline{HL}$ (If a quadrilateral is a parallelogram, then both pairs of opposite sides are congruent.)

(5) $\overline{HJ} \cong \overline{HL}$ (Transitive)

(6) $\triangle HJL$ is isosceles. (Definition of isosceles triangle)

24. **(1)** Rectangle *QPRS*, $\overline{QU} \cong \overline{SU}$ (Given)

(2) $\angle UQS \cong \angle USQ$ (Base Angles Theorem)

(3) $\overline{PR} \parallel \overline{QS}$ (Definition of rectangle-/parallelogram)

(4) $\angle PVQ \cong \angle UQS$, $\angle RTS \cong \angle USQ$ (If two parallel lines are cut by a transversal, then alternate interior angles are congruent.)

(5) $\angle RTS \cong \angle UQS$ (Transitive)

(6) $\angle PVQ \cong \angle RTS$ (Transitive)

(7) $\angle P$ and $\angle R$ are right angles (Definition of rectangle)

(8) $\angle P \cong \angle R$ (All right angles are congruent.)

(9) $\overline{PQ} \cong \overline{RS}$ (If a quadrilateral is a rectangle/parallelogram, then both pairs of opposite sides are congruent.)

(10) $\triangle PVQ \cong \triangle RTS$ (A.A.S.)

(11) $\overline{PV} \cong \overline{RT}$ (C.P.C.T.C.)

Practice 61

a. Pentagon; regular

b. Regular nonagon; interior: $140°$; exterior: $40°$

c. $e = 50$

d. $54°$, $36°$

e. **(1)** $JKLM$ is a parallelogram. (Given)

(2) $\overline{KJ} \cong \overline{LM}$ (If a quadrilateral is a parallelogram, pairs of opposite sides are congruent.)

(3) $\angle K \cong \angle M$ (If a quadrilateral is a parallelogram, pairs

of opposite angles are congruent.)

(4) $\overline{JP} \perp \overline{KL}$, $\overline{LN} \perp \overline{JM}$ (Given)

(5) $\angle JPK$ and $\angle LNM$ are right angles (Perpendicular lines intersect to form right angles.)

(6) $\angle JPK \cong \angle LNM$ (All right angles are congruent.)

(7) $\triangle KJP \cong \triangle MLN$ (A.A.S.)

Problem Set 61

1. True
2. False
3. $\dfrac{180(n-2)}{n}$
4. 180 – the measure of each interior angle; $\dfrac{360}{n}$
5. rhombus
6. Square (which is a special kind of quadrilateral); regular
7. Right triangle; not regular
8. Octagon; regular
9. Sum of interior: $180°$; sum of exterior: $360°$
10. Sum of interior: $720°$; sum of exterior: $360°$
11. Regular hexagon; interior: $120°$; exterior: $60°$
12. Regular decagon; interior: $144°$; exterior: $36°$

13. Converse: If both pairs of opposite angles are congruent, then a quadrilateral is a parallelogram; true
Inverse: If a quadrilateral is not a parallelogram, then both pairs of its opposite angles are not congruent; true
Contrapositive: If both pairs of opposite angles are not congruent, then a quadrilateral is not a parallelogram; true

14. Converse: If a quadrilateral is a parallelogram, then the diagonals bisect each other; true
Inverse: If the diagonals of a quadrilateral do not bisect each other, then a quadrilateral is not a parallelogram; true
Contrapositive: If a quadrilateral is not a parallelogram, then the diagonals do not bisect each other; true

15. The Whole is Greater than Its Part
16. If Unequal Sides, then Unequal Angles
17. The sum of the measures of the angles of a triangle is 180.
18. $y = 140$
19. $a + b + c + d = 220$
20. $r = 36$

21. $m\angle H = 30$,
$m\angle G = 120$; $\triangle FGH$
is isosceles (and
obtuse)

22. $50°$, $40°$

23. **(1)** $\overline{LQ} \cong \overline{PQ}$
(Given)
(2) $\angle LPQ \cong \angle L$
(Base Angles
Theorem)
(3) $\angle L \cong \angle HQP$
(Given)
(4) $\angle LPQ \cong \angle HQP$
(Transitive)
(5) $\overline{LP} \parallel \overline{QH}$ (If two
lines form congruent
alternate interior
angles with a trans-
versal, then the lines
are parallel.)
(6) $PLQH$ is a
trapezoid. (Definition
of trapezoid)

24. **(1)** $ABCD$ is a
parallelogram.
(Given)
(2) $\overline{AB} \cong \overline{CD}$ (If a
quadrilateral is a
parallelogram, pairs
of opposite sides are
congruent.)
(3) $\angle A \cong \angle C$ (If a
quadrilateral is a
parallelogram, pairs
of opposite angles are
congruent.)
(4) $\overline{BE} \perp \overline{AD}$,
$\overline{FD} \perp \overline{BC}$ (Given)
(5) $\angle BEA$ and
$\angle DFC$ are right
angles (Perpendicular
lines intersect to form
right angles.)

(6) $\angle BEA \cong \angle DFC$
(All right angles are
congruent.)
(7) $\triangle ABE \cong \triangle CDF$
(A.A.S.)

Practice 62

a. 36
b. 72
c. $a + b = 172$
d. 8
e. **(1)** Quadrilateral
$STUR$; $\overline{SU}$ and $\overline{TL}$
bisect each other.
(Given)
(2) $STUL$ is a parallelogram. (If the
diagonals bisect each
other, then a quad-
rilateral is a paral-
lelogram.)
(3) $\overline{ST} \parallel \overline{UL}$ and
$\overline{ST} \parallel \overline{UR}$ (Definition
of parallelogram)
(4) $STUR$ is a trap-
ezoid (Definition of
trapezoid)
(5) $\overline{SR} \cong \overline{TU}$ (Given)
(6) $STUR$ is an isos-
celes trapezoid
(Definition of isos-
celes trapezoid)
(7) $\angle R \cong \angle RUT$
(The lower base
angles of an isosceles
trapezoid are con-
gruent.)

Problem Set 62

1. True
2. True
3. regular polygon

4. $180(n-2)$
5. heptagon
6. Quadrilateral
7. Parallelogram
8. $900°$
9. $720°$
10. 30
11. 26
12. 104
13. $45°$, $60°$, $75°$; acute
14. $60°$, $60°$, $60°$
15. sometimes
16. always
17. $\overline{CD}$
18. $\overline{AC}$
19. If a quadrilateral is a
parallelogram, then
consecutive angles
are supplementary.
20. If a quadrilateral is a
parallelogram, then
both pairs of opposite
sides are congruent.
21. $x + y = 164$
22. 10
23. **(1)** $\angle RTS \cong \angle TRV$
(Given)
(2) $\overline{RV} \parallel \overline{ST}$ (If two
lines form congruent
alternate interior
angles with a trans-
versal, then the lines
are parallel.)
(3) $\overline{RV} \cong \overline{ST}$ (Given)
(4) $RSTV$ is a paral-
lelogram. (If one pair
of opposite sides is
both parallel and con-
gruent, then a quad-
rilateral is a paral-
lelogram.)
24. **(1)** Quadrilateral
$DJKL$; $\overline{JL}$ and $\overline{FK}$

bisect each other.
(Given)

(2) *FJKL* is a parallelogram. (If the diagonals bisect each other, then a quadrilateral is a parallelogram.)

(3) $\overline{JF} \parallel \overline{KL}$ and $\overline{JD} \parallel \overline{KL}$ (Definition of parallelogram)

(4) *DJKL* is a trapezoid (Definition of trapezoid)

(5) $\overline{JK} \cong \overline{DL}$ (Given)

(6) *DJKL* is an isosceles trapezoid (Definition of isosceles trapezoid)

(7) $\angle D \cong \angle DJK$ (The lower base angles of an isosceles trapezoid are congruent.)

CHAPTER 10

Practice 63

a. Yes

b. 120°, 30°, 30°

c. $x = 10$, $y = 10$

d. $m\angle E = 105$, $m\angle F = 35$

e. **(1)** Regular hexagon $OPQRST$ with diagonals $\overline{PR}$ and $\overline{TR}$ (Given)
(2) $\overline{TS} \cong \overline{PQ}$, $\overline{SR} \cong \overline{QR}$ (A regular polygon is equilateral.)
(3) $\angle S \cong \angle Q$ (A regular polygon is equiangular.)
(4) $\triangle TSR \cong \triangle PQR$ (S.A.S.)
(5) $\overline{PR} \cong \overline{TR}$ (C.P.C.T.C.)

Problem Set 63

1. True
2. True
3. $\dfrac{180(n-2)}{n}$
4. trapezoid
5. parallel; one-half
6. Regular pentagon, 108°
7. Equilateral triangle, 60°
8. 210
9. $27\dfrac{2}{3}$
10. Yes
11. Yes
12. No
13. 90°, 70°, 20°
14. 36°, 72°, 72°
15. Contrapositive
16. Converse
17. If one pair of opposite sides are both parallel and congruent, then a quadrilateral is a parallelogram.
18. If a quadrilateral is a parallelogram, then both pairs of opposite angles are congruent.
19. $x = 8$, $y = 12$
20. $w + u = 90$
21. 45°, 135°
22. $m\angle D = 104$, $m\angle R = 26$
23. **(1)** Trapezoid $ABCE$ with bases $\overline{AE}$ and $\overline{BC}$ (Given)
(2) $\overline{AE} \parallel \overline{BC}$ (Definition of trapezoid)
(3) $\overline{AD} \cong \overline{BC}$ (Given)
(4) $ABCD$ is a parallelogram.(If one pair of opposite sides is both parallel and congruent, then a quadrilateral is a parallelogram.)
24. **(1)** Regular octagon $ABCDEFGH$ with diagonals $\overline{HF}$ and $\overline{DF}$ (Given)
(2) $\overline{HG} \cong \overline{DE}$, $\overline{GF} \cong \overline{EF}$ (A regular polygon is equilateral.)
(3) $\angle G \cong \angle E$ (A regular polygon is equiangular.)
(4) $\triangle HGF \cong \triangle DEF$ (S.A.S.)
(5) $\overline{HF} \cong \overline{DF}$ (C.P.C.T.C.)

Practice 64

a. 52

b. 18

c. $y = 19$

d. 208 lip synchers

e. **(1)** F is the midpoint of $\overline{EJ}$ and G is the midpoint of $\overline{DJ}$ (Given)
(2) $\overline{ED} \parallel \overline{FG}$ (The line segment joining the midpoints of two sides of a triangle is parallel to the third side and is one-half of its length.)
(3) $m\angle FGJ = m\angle D$ (If two parallel lines are cut by a transversal, then their corresponding angles are congruent.)
(4) $m\angle FGJ > m\angle J$ (Given)
(5) $m\angle D > m\angle J$ (Substitution)
(6) $EJ > DE$ (If Unequal Angles, then Unequal Sides)

Problem Set 64

1. False
2. False
3. geometric mean
4. cross-multiply
5. rhombus
6. 540°

7. 1,260°
8. 21
9. 42
10. means: 4, 24; extremes: 3, 32
11. means: t, u; extremes: s, v
12. 8
13. 10
14. $x = 7$
15. $y = 11$
16. $\angle B$
17. $\angle X$
18. $x = 70$
19. $x = 60$, $y = 20$, $z = 30$
20. $d = 24$
21. 12
22. 46,875 men subscribers
23. (1) $\overline{AB} \cong \overline{DC}$, $\overline{AD} \cong \overline{BC}$ (Given)
    (2) $ABCD$ is a parallelogram (If both pairs of opposite sides are congruent, then a quadrilateral is a parallelogram.)
    (3) $\angle A$ and $\angle B$ are supplementary. (If a quadrilateral is a parallelogram, then consecutive angles are supplementary.)
24. (1) P is the midpoint of $\overline{CL}$ and V is the midpoint of $\overline{CT}$ (Given)
    (2) $\overline{LT} \parallel \overline{PV}$ (The line segment joining the midpoints of two sides of a triangle is parallel to the third

side and is one-half of its length.)
(3) $m\angle PVC = m\angle T$ (If two parallel lines are cut by a transversal, then their corresponding angles are congruent.)
(4) $m\angle PVC > m\angle C$ (Given)
(5) $m\angle T > m\angle C$ (Substitution)
(6) $CL > LT$ (If Unequal Angles, then Unequal Sides)

Practice 65
a. $2r + 2s$
b. $g = \dfrac{bv}{u}$
c. Yes
d. 3,000 dogs
e. (1) Rhombus $ABCD$ with diagonals $\overline{AC}$ and $\overline{BD}$ (Given)
   (2) $\overline{AC} \perp \overline{BD}$ (The diagonals of a rhombus are perpendicular to each other.)
   (3) $\angle BOC$ is a right angle. (Perpendicular lines intersect to form right angles.)
   (4) ΔBOC is a right triangle (Definition of right triangle)
   (5) $\angle OBC$ and $\angle OCB$ are complementary. (The acute angles of a right triangle are complementary.)

Problem Set 65
1. True
2. False
3. True
4. twice
5. proportion
6. Rhombus
7. Isosceles trapezoid
8. 29
9. $2u + 2v$
10. No
11. No
12. 14
13. $\sqrt{66}$
14. $x = 48$
15. $q = \dfrac{pt}{s}$
16. Yes
17. No
18. Yes
19. $s + u = 250$
20. $x = 21$
21. 224
22. 2,000 calls
23. (1) $\overline{GI}$ and $\overline{FH}$ are altitudes to $\overline{DH}$ and $\overline{DG}$ (Given)
    (2) $\angle GIH$ and $\angle HFG$ are right angles. (Definition of altitude)
    (3) $\angle GIH \cong \angle HFG$ (All right angles are congruent.)
    (4) $\angle HGF \cong \angle IHG$ (Given)
    (5) $\overline{GH} \cong \overline{GH}$ (Reflexive)
    (6) $\Delta GIH \cong \Delta HFG$ (A.A.S.)
    (7) $\overline{GI} \cong \overline{FH}$ (C.P.C.T.C.)

24. **(1)** Rhombus *RTUV* with diagonals $\overline{RU}$ and $\overline{TV}$ (Given)
(2) $\overline{RU} \perp \overline{TV}$ (The diagonals of a rhombus are perpendicular to each other.)
(3) $\angle TQU$ is a right angle. (Perpendicular lines intersect to form right angles.)
(4) ΔTQU is a right triangle (Definition of right triangle)
(5) $\angle QTU$ and $\angle QUT$ are complementary. (The acute angles of a right triangle are complementary.)

Practice 66
a. Yes
b. 12.78 : 1 (or just 12.78)
c. $a = 112.5$
d. 20 grams
e. **(1)** Rhombus *FGHI* (Given)
(2) $\overline{GI}$ and $\overline{FH}$ are perpendicular (The diagonals of a rhombus are perpendicular.)
(3) $\angle HPG$ and $\angle FPG$ are right angles (Perpendicular lines intersect to form right angles.)
(4) $\angle HPG \cong \angle FPG$ (All right angles are congruent.)

(5) $\overline{FP} \cong \overline{PH}$ (If a quadrilateral is a rhombus/parallelogram, then the diagonals bisect each other.)
(6) $\overline{JP} \cong \overline{JP}$ (Reflexive)
(7) $\Delta FJP \cong \Delta HJP$ (S.A.S.)
(8) $\overline{FJ} \cong \overline{JH}$ (C.P.C.T.C.)
(9) ΔFJH is isosceles. (Definition of isosceles triangle)

Problem Set 66
1. False
2. False
3. Similar figures
4. regular polygon
5. geometric mean
6. Rhombus; No
7. Parallelogram; No
8. No
9. Yes
10. always
11. always
12. 1 : 7
13. 28.8 : 1 (or just 28.8)
14. 12
15. $b = \dfrac{mt}{v}$
16. If two angles are supplementary to the same angle, then they are congruent.
17. If Unequal Angles, then Unequal Sides
18. $x = 68$
19. $y = 100$
20. $z = 90$
21. 25 feet
22. 8 grams

23. **(1)** $RS = TU$, $\angle VTR \cong \angle WSU$, $\angle VRT \cong \angle WUS$ (Given)
(2) $ST = ST$ (Reflexive)

(3) $RS + ST = ST + TU$ (Addition)
(4) $RT = SU$ (Betweenness of points)
(5) $\Delta RVT \cong \Delta UWS$ (A.S.A.)

24. **(1)** Rhombus *ABCD* (Given)
(2) $\overline{DB}$ and $\overline{AC}$ are perpendicular (The diagonals of a rhombus are perpendicular.)
(3) $\angle DOC$ and $\angle COB$ are right angles (Perpendicular lines intersect to form right angles.)
(4) $\angle DOC \cong \angle COB$ (All right angles are congruent.)
(5) $\overline{DO} \cong \overline{OB}$ (If a quadrilateral is a rhombus/parallelogram, then the diagonals bisect each other.)
(6) $\overline{OP} \cong \overline{OP}$ (Reflexive)
(7) $\Delta DOP \cong \Delta BOP$ (S.A.S.)
(8) $\overline{DP} \cong \overline{PB}$ (C.P.C.T.C.)
(9) ΔDPB is isosceles. (Definition of isosceles triangle)

Practice 67

a. $\dfrac{KQ}{MQ} = \dfrac{KV}{UV}$

b. $\dfrac{HJ}{HP} = \dfrac{5}{2}$; $\dfrac{IJ}{IK} = \dfrac{5}{2}$;
Sides are divided proportionally.

c. $2x + 2y$

d. $x = 42$

e. **(1)** $\triangle MCA$ and rectangle $BCDN$ (Given)

(2) $\overline{BC} \parallel \overline{ND}$ and $\overline{BN} \parallel \overline{CD}$ (Definition of a rectangle/parallelogram)

(3) $\dfrac{DM}{DC} = \dfrac{MN}{NA}$ and $\dfrac{MN}{NA} = \dfrac{BC}{AB}$ (If a line is parallel to one side of a triangle and intersects the other two sides, then the line divides those sides proportionally.)

(4) $\dfrac{DM}{DC} = \dfrac{BC}{AB}$ (Transitive)

Problem Set 67

1. True
2. True
3. $180(n-2)$
4. congruent
5. not congruent; greater; longer
6. Regular pentagon, 108°
7. Regular hexagon, 120°

8. $\dfrac{LS}{SP} = \dfrac{LT}{TR}$

9. $\dfrac{LP}{LS} = \dfrac{LR}{LT}$

10. $\dfrac{EC}{BE} = \dfrac{3}{4}$; $\dfrac{OA}{BO} = \dfrac{3}{4}$;
Sides are divided proportionally.

11. $\dfrac{BA}{OA} = \dfrac{7}{3}$; $\dfrac{BC}{EC} = \dfrac{7}{3}$;
Sides are divided proportionally.

12. $2a + 2b$
13. 28
14. $x = 36$

15. $y = \dfrac{m}{3}$

16. $\angle C$ is smallest.
17. $\angle X$ is largest.
18. $x = 65$
19. $y = 40$
20. $x = 80$
21. 54°
22. 30°, 150°
23. **(1)** B is the midpoint of $\overline{AC}$ and D is the midpoint of $\overline{CE}$ (Given)

(2) $AB = \dfrac{1}{2} AC$ and $ED = \dfrac{1}{2} CE$ (Definition of midpoint)

(3) $m\angle E > m\angle A$ (Given)

(4) $AC > CE$ (If Unequal Angles, then Unequal Sides)

(5) $\dfrac{1}{2} AC > \dfrac{1}{2} CE$ (Multiplication Property of Inequality)

(6) $AB > ED$ (Substitution)

24. **(1)** $\triangle DHF$ and rectangle $EJPH$ (Given)

(2) $\overline{EJ} \parallel \overline{PH}$ and $\overline{EP} \parallel \overline{JH}$ (Definition of a rectangle/parallelogram)

(3) $\dfrac{FJ}{JH} = \dfrac{FE}{ED}$ and $\dfrac{FE}{ED} = \dfrac{HP}{PD}$ (If a line is parallel to one side of a triangle and intersects the other two sides, then the line divides those sides proportionally.)

(4) $\dfrac{FJ}{JH} = \dfrac{HP}{PD}$ (Transitive)

Practice 68

a. $\dfrac{BP}{PC} = \dfrac{4}{5}$; $\dfrac{AM}{MC} = \dfrac{8}{11}$;
$\overline{AB}$ is not parallel to $\overline{PM}$.

b. $1:5$

c. Yes

d. 36 men

e. **(1)** $\triangle ABC$ with altitudes $\overline{AK}$ and $\overline{CJ}$ (Given)

(2) $\overline{AK} \perp \overline{BC}$ and $\overline{CJ} \perp \overline{AB}$ (Definition of altitude)

(3) $\angle AKC$ and $\angle CJA$ are right angles (Perpendicular lines intersect to form right angles.)

(4) $\angle AKC \cong \angle CJA$ (All right angles are congruent.)

(5) $\angle JOA \cong \angle KOC$ (Pairs of vertical angles are congruent.)

(6) $\triangle JOA \sim \triangle KOC$ (A.A. Similarity)

Problem Set 68

1. True
2. True
3. Base Angles Theorem
4. consecutive
5. diagonals
6. 900°
7. 360°
8. $\dfrac{BW}{WC} = \dfrac{5}{6}$; $\dfrac{AT}{TC} = \dfrac{5}{6}$; The sides are divided proportionally.
9. $\dfrac{BC}{BW} = \dfrac{11}{5}$; $\dfrac{AC}{AT} = \dfrac{11}{5}$; The sides are divided proportionally.
10. $\dfrac{GI}{FG} = \dfrac{2}{3}$; $\dfrac{HE}{FH} = \dfrac{13}{19}$; $\overline{IE}$ is not parallel to $\overline{GH}$.
11. $\dfrac{FI}{IG} = \dfrac{1}{2}$; $\dfrac{FE}{EH} = \dfrac{6}{13}$; $\overline{IE}$ is not parallel to $\overline{GH}$.
12. 16
13. 21
14. 1 : 48
15. 1 : 2
16. Yes
17. Yes

18. Yes
19. 100°
20. 130°
21. 27 grams
22. 24 girls
23. **(1)** $\overline{AC} \cong \overline{CE}$ (Given)

(2) $\angle A \cong \angle E$ (Base Angles Theorem)

(3) $\overline{RZ} \perp \overline{AE}$, $\overline{LV} \perp \overline{AE}$ (Given)

(4) $\angle RZE$ and $\angle LVA$ are right angles. (Perpendicular lines intersect to form right angles.)

(5) $\angle RZE \cong \angle LVA$ (All right angles are congruent.)

(6) $\triangle RZE \sim \triangle LVA$ (A.A. Similarity)

24. **(1)** $\triangle PRD$ with altitudes $\overline{LD}$ and $\overline{PS}$ (Given)

(2) $\overline{LD} \perp \overline{PR}$ and $\overline{PS} \perp \overline{RD}$ (Definition of altitude)

(3) $\angle RLD$ and $\angle PSD$ are right angles (Perpendicular lines intersect to form right angles.)

(4) $\angle RLD \cong \angle PSD$ (All right angles are congruent.)

(5) $\angle LEP \cong \angle SED$ (Pairs of vertical angles are congruent.)

(6) $\triangle LEP \sim \triangle SED$ (A.A. Similarity)

Practice 69

a. $? = 15$; $x = 14$
b. None
c. $x = 130$
d. 48°, 132°, 48°, 132°
e. **(1)** $\triangle ABC \sim \triangle PLM$ (Given)

(2) $\angle ABC \cong \angle PLM$, $\angle ACB \cong \angle PML$ (Converse of Definition of Similar Triangles)

(3) $\triangle ABC \sim \triangle XYZ$ (Given)

(4) $\angle ABC \cong \angle XYZ$, $\angle ACB \cong \angle XZY$ (Converse of Definition of Similar Triangles)

(5) $\angle PLM \cong \angle XYZ$, $\angle PML \cong \angle XZY$ (Transitive)

(6) $\triangle PLM \sim \triangle XYZ$ (A.A. Similarity)

Problem Set 69

1. True
2. True
3. regular polygon
4. isosceles trapezoid
5. Exterior Angle Inequality Theorem
6. Inverse
7. Contrapositive
8. $? = 9$; $x = 12$
9. $? = 24$; $x = 12$
10. $p = 14$
11. $k = \dfrac{17}{3}$
12. 29 inches
13. 63 centimeters
14. Exterior Angle of a Triangle Theorem

15. If Unequal Angles, then Unequal Sides
16. S.A.S. Similarity
17. S.S.S. Similarity
18. None
19. $x = 75$
20. $y = 120$
21. 112 inches
22. $60°$, $120°$, $60°$, $120°$
23. **(1)** $\overline{KI} \cong \overline{IL}$, $\overline{NM} \cong \overline{ML}$ (Given)
    (2) $\dfrac{KI}{NM} = \dfrac{IL}{ML}$ (Division)
    (3) $\angle KIL \cong \angle NML$ (Given)
    (4) $\triangle KIL \sim \triangle NML$ (S.A.S. Similarity)
24. **(1)** $\triangle ABC \sim \triangle PLM$ (Given)
    (2) $\angle ABC \cong \angle PLM$, $\angle ACB \cong \angle PML$ (Converse of Definition of Similar Triangles)
    (3) $\triangle PLM \sim \triangle XYZ$ (Given)
    (4) $\angle PLM \cong \angle XYZ$, $\angle PML \cong \angle XZY$ (Converse of Definition of Similar Triangles)
    (5) $\angle ABC \cong \angle XYZ$, $\angle ACB \cong \angle XZY$ (Transitive)
    (6) $\triangle ABC \sim \triangle XYZ$ (A.A. Similarity)

Practice 70

a. There are several possibilities. Here are

two: $\dfrac{AB}{CD} = \dfrac{LM}{JK}$ or $\dfrac{JK}{CD} = \dfrac{LM}{AB}$

b. A.A. Similarity
c. Converse of Definition of Similar Triangles
d. 84 inches
e. **(1)** $\overline{KL} \parallel \overline{MN}$ and $\overline{JL} \parallel \overline{ON}$ (Given)
   (2) $\angle K \cong \angle M$, $\angle O \cong \angle J$ (If two parallel lines are cut by a transversal, then their corresponding angles are congruent.)
   (3) $\triangle JKL \sim \triangle OMN$ (A.A. Similarity)
   (4) $\dfrac{KL}{MN} = \dfrac{JL}{ON}$ (Definition of Similar Figures)
   (5) $KL \times ON = MN \times JL$ (In a proportion, the product of the means is equal to the product of the extremes.)

Problem Set 70

1. True
2. True
3. similar
4. parallel
5. $180(n-2)$
6. $360°$
7. $360°$
8. There are several possibilities. Here are

two: $\dfrac{3}{2} = \dfrac{18}{12}$ or $\dfrac{12}{2} = \dfrac{18}{3}$

9. There are several possibilities. Here are two: $\dfrac{AT}{EG} = \dfrac{AN}{EK}$ or $\dfrac{EK}{EG} = \dfrac{AN}{AT}$
10. $24 + k$
11. 32
12. $\angle P$
13. $\overline{XZ}$
14. A.A. Similarity
15. S.A.S. Similarity
16. A.A. Similarity
17. Converse of Definition of Similar Triangles
18. Converse of Definition of Similar Triangles
19. $x = 100$
20. $y = 30$
21. 77 kennel guests
22. 70 inches
23. **(1)** $\triangle JKL \sim \triangle STV$ (Given)
    (2) $m\angle L = m\angle V$ and $m\angle JKL = m\angle STV$ (Converse of Definition of Similar Triangles)
    (3) $\dfrac{1}{2} m\angle JKL = \dfrac{1}{2} m\angle STV$ (Multiplication)
    (4) $\overline{KP}$ bisects $\angle JKL$, and $\overline{TO}$ bisects $\angle STV$ (Given)

(5) $\frac{1}{2}m\angle JKL$
$= m\angle PKL$ and
$\frac{1}{2}m\angle STV = m\angle OTV$
(Definition of angle bisector)
(6) $m\angle PKL$
$= m\angle OTV$
(Substitution)
(7) $\Delta KPL \sim \Delta TOV$
(A.A. Similarity)

24. **(1)** $\overline{AB} \parallel \overline{DE}$,
$\overline{CB} \parallel \overline{FE}$ (Given)
(2) $\angle A \cong \angle FDE$,
$\angle DFE \cong \angle C$ (If two parallel lines are cut by a transversal, then their corresponding angles are congruent.)
(3) $\Delta ABC \sim \Delta DEF$ (A.A. Similarity)
(4) $\dfrac{DE}{AB} = \dfrac{FE}{CB}$
(Converse of Definition of Similar Triangles)
(5) $DE \times CB$
$= AB \times FE$ (In a proportion, the product of the means is equal to the product of the extremes.)

Practice 71

a. $x = -3a + (-4b)$
b. If a line intersects two sides of a triangle and divides those sides proportionally, then the line

is parallel to the third side.
c. perimeter $= 12$
d. $WC = 8$, $PO = 10$
e. **(1)** $\overline{GJ} \parallel \overline{DF}$ (Given)
(2) $\angle IHF \cong GIH$ (If two parallel lines are cut by a transversal, then their alternate interior angles are congruent.)
(3) $\overline{GH} \parallel \overline{EF}$ (Given)
(4) $\angle HEF \cong \angle IHG$ (If two parallel lines are cut by a transversal, then their alternate interior angles are congruent.)
(5) $\Delta HEF \sim \Delta IHG$ (A.A. Similarity)
(6) $\dfrac{EF}{HG} = \dfrac{HF}{IG}$
(Converse of Definition of Similar Triangles)
(7) $HG \times HF$
$= IG \times EF$ (In a proportion, the product of the means is equal to the product of the extremes.)

Problem Set 71

1. True
2. False
3. False
4. similar
5. parallel
6. Parallelogram
7. Rectangle
8. sometimes
9. always

10. $d - \dfrac{1}{2}a$
11. $m\angle AOC = 51$
12. $x = \dfrac{3a}{2}$
13. $y = 2a + 3b$
14. If a line intersects two sides of a triangle and divides those sides proportionally, then the line is parallel to the third side.
15. S.S.S. Similarity
16. A.A. Similarity or S.A.S. Similarity
17. S.S.S. Similarity
18. $x = 50$
19. $y = 45$
20. perimeter $= 18$
21. $BT = 18$, $DA = 6$
22. $FQ = 8$, $AP = 12$
23. **(1)** ΔDFC, ΔBAC, and $\dfrac{FC}{AC} = \dfrac{DC}{BC}$
(Given)
(2) $\angle C \cong \angle C$ (Reflexive)
(3) $\Delta DFC \sim \Delta BAC$ (S.A.S. Similarity)
(4) $\dfrac{\text{perimeter } \Delta DFC}{\text{perimeter } \Delta BAC}$
$= \dfrac{FD}{AB}$ (If two triangles are similar, then their perimeters have the same ratio as any pair of corresponding sides.)
24. **(1)** $\overline{VZ} \parallel \overline{TR}$ (Given)
(2) $\angle WUT \cong \angle ZWU$ (If two parallel lines are cut by a transver-

sal, then their alternate interior angles are congruent.)

(3) $\overline{ZU} \parallel \overline{ST}$ (Given)

(4) $\angle UST \cong ZUW$ (If two parallel lines are cut by a transversal, then their alternate interior angles are congruent.)

(5) $\Delta UST \sim \Delta WUZ$ (A.A. Similarity)

(6) $\dfrac{ZU}{ST} = \dfrac{ZW}{TU}$ (Converse of definition of similar triangles)

(7) $ZU \times TU = ZW \times ST$ (In a proportion, the product of the means is equal to the product of the extremes.)

CHAPTER 11

Practice 72

a. $y = 15$

b. $a = 20$

c. perimeter $= 35$

d. $x = 10$

e. **(1)** $\overline{KM}$ bisects $\angle LMN$ (Given)
(2) $\angle KML \cong \angle KMN$ (Definition of angle bisector)
(3) $LK = KM$ (Given)
(4) $\angle KLM \cong \angle KML$ (Base Angles Theorem)
(5) $\angle KLM \cong \angle KMN$ (Substitution or Transitive)
(6) $\angle N \cong \angle N$ (Reflexive)
(7) $\triangle NMK \sim \triangle NLM$ (A.A. Similarity)
(8) $\dfrac{LN}{MN} = \dfrac{MN}{KN}$ (Converse of Definition of Similar Triangles)

Problem Set 72

1. True
2. True
3. similar
4. similar
5. parallel; one-half
6. $\dfrac{RU}{US} = \dfrac{2}{3}$; $\dfrac{TV}{VS} = \dfrac{2}{3}$; $\overline{RT}$ is parallel to $\overline{UV}$.

7. $\dfrac{US}{RS} = \dfrac{3}{5}$; $\dfrac{VS}{TS} = \dfrac{3}{5}$; $\overline{RT}$ is parallel to $\overline{UV}$.

8. $y = 20$
9. $x = 16$
10. $\angle E$
11. $m\angle H = 92$; $\overline{JI}$ is the longest side
12. Angle-Side-Angle or Angle-Angle-Side
13. Hypotenuse-Leg
14. Converse of Definition of Similar Triangles
15. If two triangles are similar, then the lengths of a pair of corresponding altitudes have the same ratio as the lengths of any pair of corresponding sides.
16. $x = 30$
17. $y = 6.5$
18. $x = 36$
19. perimeter $= 27$
20. perimeter $= 33$
21. 54 acrobats
22. $HI = 6$; $DJ = 8$
23. **(1)** $\overline{DE}$ is an altitude of right $\triangle BCD$ (Given)
(2) $\dfrac{EC}{CD} = \dfrac{CD}{BC}$ (The altitude to the hypotenuse of a right triangle forms two triangles that are similar to each other and to the original triangle.)
(3) $CD = BE$ (Given)

(4) $\dfrac{EC}{BE} = \dfrac{BE}{BC}$ (Substitution)

24. **(1)** $\overline{SR}$ bisects $\angle PRQ$ (Given)
(2) $\angle PRS \cong \angle QRS$ (Definition of angle bisector)
(3) $PS = SR$ (Given)
(4) $\angle SPR \cong \angle PRS$ (Base Angles Theorem)
(5) $\angle SPR \cong \angle QRS$ (Substitution or Transitive)
(6) $\angle Q \cong \angle Q$ (Reflexive)
(7) $\triangle QRS \sim \triangle QPR$ (A.A. Similarity)
(8) $\dfrac{PQ}{RQ} = \dfrac{RQ}{SQ}$ (Converse of Definition of Similar Triangles)

Practice 73

a. $x = 12$

b. $QO = 20$

c. $RT = 14$; $KM = 21$

d. 8.66

e. **(1)** $p^2 + q^2 = m^2$ (Given)
(2) Draw right $\triangle WRT$ with legs p and q. (Definition of right triangle)
(3) $p^2 + q^2 = n^2$ (Pythagorean Theorem)
(4) $m^2 = n^2$ (Substitution)

(5) $m = n$ (Take square root of both sides.)
(6) $\triangle QMP \cong \triangle WRT$ (S.S.S.)
(7) $\angle M$ is a right angle (C.P.C.T.C.)
(8) $\triangle QMP$ is a right triangle. (Definition of right triangle)

Problem Set 73
1. True
2. True
3. right triangle
4. similar
5. rhombus
6. Regular octagon; 135°
7. Regular decagon; 144°
8. 90°, 72°, 18°
9. 77°, 77°, 26°
10. $x = 6$
11. $x = 13$
12. $7 : 5$
13. $1 : 20$
14. $\dfrac{DL}{KD} = \dfrac{4}{5}$; $\dfrac{CM}{KC} = \dfrac{4}{5}$; Sides are divided proportionally.
15. $\dfrac{DL}{KL} = \dfrac{4}{9}$; $\dfrac{CM}{KM} = \dfrac{4}{9}$; Sides are divided proportionally.
16. $y = 120$
17. $x = 14$
18. $FH = 10$
19. None
20. A.A. Similarity
21. $BC = 12$; $EF = 16$
22. 10.39
23. **(1)** $\overline{DP}$ bisects $\angle ADS$ (Given)

(2) $m\angle ADP = m\angle PDS$ (Definition of angle bisector)
(3) $m\angle DPA > m\angle PDS$ (The measure of an exterior angle of a triangle is greater than the measure of either of the remote interior angles.)
(4) $m\angle DPA > m\angle ADP$ (Substitution)
(5) $DA > PA$ (If Unequal Angles, then Unequal Sides)
24. **(1)** $a^2 + b^2 = c^2$ (Given)
(2) Draw right $\triangle EFG$ with legs a and b. (Definition of right triangle)
(3) $a^2 + b^2 = n^2$ (Pythagorean Theorem)
(4) $c^2 = n^2$ (Substitution)
(5) $c = n$ (Take square root of both sides)
(6) $\triangle ABC \cong \triangle EFG$ (S.S.S.)
(7) $\angle C$ is a right angle. (C.P.C.T.C.)
(8) $\triangle ABC$ is a right triangle. (Definition of right triangle)

Practice 74
a. 13.44
b. $y = 2\sqrt{13}$
c. $x = 60$

d. $WX = 27$; $WZ = 21$
e. **(1)** $FGHJ$ is an isosceles trapezoid with $\overline{FJ} \cong \overline{GH}$. (Given)
(2) $\angle JFG \cong \angle HGF$ (The base angles of an isosceles trapezoid are congruent.)
(3) $\overline{FG} \cong \overline{FG}$ (Reflexive)
(4) $\triangle FHG \cong \triangle GJF$ (S.A.S.)
(5) $\overline{FH} \cong \overline{GJ}$ (C.P.C.T.C.)

Problem Set 74
1. False
2. True
3. Pythagorean Triple
4. diagonals
5. similar
6. 3.32
7. 7.95
8. $? = 6$
9. $? = 17$
10. $x = 4$
11. $y = 2\sqrt{5}$
12. $6y + 12$
13. 24
14. Pythagorean Theorem
15. Converse of Pythagorean Theorem
16. $x = 3q + 4p$
17. $y = \dfrac{5t - 3r}{2}$
18. $x = 27$
19. $y = 40$
20. Side-Side-Side
21. None
22. $JK = 68$; $JL = 128$

23. $ST = 75$; $TV = 25$

24. **(1)** $\triangle TPS \sim \triangle VWR$
$\overline{UR}$ bisects $\angle WRT$
(Given)
(2) $\angle PST \cong \angle WRV$
(Converse of
definition of similar
triangles)
(3) $\angle WRV \cong \angle VRP$
(Definition of angle
bisector)
(4) $\angle PST \cong \angle VRP$
(Transitive or
Substitution)
(5) $\angle TPS \cong \angle VPR$
(Pairs of vertical
angles are
congruent.)
(6) $\triangle TPS \sim \triangle VPR$
(A.A. Similarity)

25. **(1)** $ABCD$ is an
isosceles trapezoid
with $\overline{AB} \cong \overline{CD}$.
(Given)
(2) $\angle BAD \cong \angle CDA$
(The base angles of
an isosceles trapezoid
are congruent.)
(3) $\overline{AD} \cong \overline{AD}$
(Reflexive)
(4) $\triangle BAD \cong \triangle CDA$
(S.A.S.)
(5) $\overline{AC} \cong \overline{BD}$
(C.P.C.T.C.)

Practice 75

a. $\dfrac{11}{\sqrt{2}}$ or $\dfrac{11\sqrt{2}}{2}$ (fully
simplified)

b. $6\sqrt{2}$

c. $x = 35$

d. 48.84

e. **(1)** Quadrilateral
$JKLM$ with diagonals
$\overline{MK}$ and $\overline{JL}$; $\overline{MK}$
bisects $\overline{JL}$ at O.
(Given)
(2) $\overline{JO} \cong \overline{LO}$
(Definition of
segment bisector)
(3) $\angle JOK \cong \angle LOM$
(Pairs of vertical
angles are con-
gruent.)
(4) $\angle LJK \cong \angle JLM$
(Given)
(5) $\triangle JOK \cong \triangle LOM$
(A.S.A.)
(6) $\overline{JK} \cong \overline{ML}$
(C.P.C.T.C.)
(7) $\overline{JK} \parallel \overline{ML}$ (If two
lines form congruent
alternate interior
angles with a trans-
versal, then the lines
are parallel.)
(8) $JKLM$ is a parallelogram. (If one pair
of sides is both
parallel and con-
gruent, then a
quadrilateral is a
parallelogram.)

Problem Set 75

1. False
2. True
3. parallel
4. legs; hypotenuse
5. If b, then a
6. Parallelogram
7. Isosceles trapezoid
8. Yes
9. No
10. $14\sqrt{2}$

11. $QE = 7$, $QW = 7\sqrt{2}$

12. $\dfrac{17}{\sqrt{2}}$ or $\dfrac{17\sqrt{2}}{2}$ (fully
simplified)

13. $5\sqrt{2}$

14. $5\sqrt{6}$

15. $y = 90$, $z = 125$

16. $x = 85$

17. $x = 105$

18. A.A. Similarity

19. S.S.S. Similarity

20. $m\angle L = 32$, $PR = 6$

21. 12, 15

22. 48.16

23. **(1)** Parallelogram
$DEFG$ (Given)
(2) $\overline{DG} \parallel \overline{EF}$ and
$\overline{DK} \parallel \overline{MF}$ (Definition of parallelo-
gram)
(3) $\angle FGD \cong \angle FED$
(If a quadrilateral is a
parallelogram, then
both pairs of opposite
angles are
congruent.)
(4) $\angle FGD$ and
$\angle LGK$ are
supplementary;
$\angle FED$ and $\angle MEN$
are supplementary (If
two angles are a
linear pair, then they
are supplementary.)
(5) $\angle KGL \cong \angle MEN$
(If two angles are
supplementary to
congruent angles,
then they are
congruent.)
(6) $\angle M \cong \angle K$ (If
two parallel lines are
cut by a transversal,

then their alternate interior angles are congruent.)
(7) $\overline{KL} \cong \overline{MN}$ (Given)
(8) $\triangle KGL \cong \triangle MEN$ (A.A.S.)
(9) $\overline{GL} \cong \overline{EN}$ (C.P.C.T.C.)

24. (1) Quadrilateral *QRST* with diagonals $\overline{QS}$ and $\overline{RT}$; $\overline{RT}$ bisects $\overline{QS}$ at *P*. (Given)
(2) $\overline{QP} \cong \overline{SP}$ (Definition of segment bisector)
(3) $\angle RPS \cong \angle TPQ$ (Pairs of vertical angles are congruent.)
(4) $\angle SQT \cong \angle RSQ$ (Given)
(5) $\triangle RPS \cong \triangle TPQ$ (A.S.A.)
(6) $\overline{RS} \cong \overline{QT}$ (C.P.C.T.C.)
(7) $\overline{RS} \parallel \overline{QT}$ (If two lines form congruent alternate interior angles with a transversal, then the lines are parallel.)
(8) *QRST* is a parallelogram. (If one pair of sides is both parallel and congruent, then a quadrilateral is a parallelogram.)

Practice 76

a. $7\sqrt{2}$; 9.87
b. 8 inches
c. $p = \dfrac{2q}{5}$
d. 13.93 feet
e. (1) $\overline{KJ} \perp \overline{JM}$; $\overline{MN} \perp \overline{KN}$; $\overline{LN} \perp \overline{JM}$ (Given)
(2) $\angle KJO$, $\angle ONM$, and $\angle NLM$ are right angles. (Perpendicular lines intersect to form right angles.)
(3) $\angle KJO \cong \angle ONM$ (All right angles are congruent.)
(4) $\angle JOK \cong \angle NOM$ (Pairs of vertical angles are congruent.)
(5) $\triangle JOK \sim \triangle NOM$ (A.A. Similarity)
(6) $\angle K \cong \angle M$ (Converse of definition of similar triangles)
(7) $\angle KJO \cong \angle NLM$ (All right angles are congruent.)
(8) $\triangle KJO \sim \triangle MLN$ (A.A. Similarity)

Problem Set 76

1. True
2. True
3. isosceles right triangle
4. interior; supplementary
5. acute
6. $4\sqrt{2}$, 5.64
7. $3\sqrt{5}$; 6.72
8. 26
9. $3\sqrt{3}$
10. 7 inches
11. 4 inches
12. $1:2$
13. $7:6$
14. 33.80
15. 42.10
16. $x = 78$
17. $y = 6$
18. $t = \dfrac{r}{3}$
19. In a 30-60 right triangle, the length of the hypotenuse is twice the length of the short leg, and the length of the long leg is $\sqrt{3}$ times the short leg.
20. In an isosceles right triangle, the length of the hypotenuse is $\sqrt{2}$ times the length of one leg.
21. 15 feet
22. 12.53 feet
23. (1) $\overline{LP} \cong \overline{LK}$ (Given)
(2) $\angle P \cong \angle LKM$ (Base Angles Theorem)
(3) $\overline{PK}$ bisects $\angle LKN$ (Given)
(4) $\angle LKM \cong \angle NKM$ (Definition of angle bisector)
(5) $\angle P \cong \angle NKM$ (Transitive or Substitution)
(6) $\angle LMP \cong \angle KMN$ (Pairs of vertical angles are congruent.)

67

(7) $\triangle LMP \sim \triangle NMK$ (A.A. Similarity)

(8) $\dfrac{LP}{NK} = \dfrac{MP}{MK}$ (Converse of definition of similar triangles)

24. **(1)** $\overline{AD} \perp \overline{DE}$; $\overline{AB} \perp \overline{BE}$; $\overline{BF} \perp \overline{AD}$ (Given)

(2) $\angle BFA$, $\angle ABC$, and $\angle CDE$ are right angles. (Perpendicular lines intersect to form right angles.)

(3) $\angle ABC \cong \angle CDE$ (All right angles are congruent.)

(4) $\angle BCA \cong \angle DCE$ (Pairs of vertical angles are congruent.)

(5) $\triangle BCA \sim \triangle DCE$ (A.A. Similarity)

(6) $\angle A \cong \angle E$ (Converse of definition of similar triangles)

(7) $\angle BFA \cong \angle CDE$ (All right angles are congruent.)

(8) $\triangle FAB \sim \triangle DEC$ (A.A. Similarity)

Practice 77

a. $\sqrt{BC \times CD}$

b. 90

c. $x = 4$

d. 55 ring tones

e. **(1)** $\angle JML$ and $\angle KNL$ are complements of $\angle JMN$ (Given)

(2) $\angle JML \cong \angle KNL$ (Complements of the same angle are congruent.)

(3) $\overline{JL} \perp \overline{ML}$ and $\overline{KL} \perp \overline{NL}$ (Given)

(4) $\angle JLM$ and $\angle KLN$ are right angles (Perpendicular lines intersect to form right angles)

(5) $\angle JLM \cong \angle KLN$ (All right angles are congruent.)

(6) $\overline{JM} \cong \overline{KN}$ (Given)

(7) $\triangle JML \cong \triangle KNL$ (A.A.S.)

(8) $\overline{ML} \cong \overline{NL}$ (C.P.C.T.C.)

(9) $\triangle LMN$ is isosceles (Definition of isosceles triangle)

Problem Set 77

1. True
2. True
3. consecutive
4. equal to, two
5. congruent
6. $\dfrac{DE}{DF}$
7. $\dfrac{EF}{DE}$
8. $3\sqrt{5}$
9. $\sqrt{AB \times CD}$
10. $? = 8$; $x = 15$
11. $? = 20$; $x = 15$
12. $FS = 20$, $QU = 24$
13. 96
14. $x = 2\sqrt{21}$
15. $y = 2\sqrt{70}$
16. A.A.S.
17. A.A.S.
18. $x = 20$
19. $y = 50$
20. $z = 5$
21. 24 hits
22. 60 pieces of candy
23. **(1)** T is the midpoint of $\overline{PS}$. (Given)

(2) $PT = TS$ (Definition of midpoint)

(3) $\angle P \cong \angle S$ (Given)

(4). $\overline{VP} \cong \overline{VS}$ (Converse of Base Angles Theorem)

(5). $\triangle TVP \cong \triangle TVS$ (S.A.S.)

24. **(1)** $\angle BCE$ and $\angle DFE$ are complements of $\angle BCF$ (Given)

(2) $\angle BCE \cong \angle DFE$ (Complements of the same angle are congruent.)

(3) $\overline{BC} \perp \overline{BE}$ and $\overline{DE} \perp \overline{DF}$ (Given)

(4) $\angle CBE$ and $\angle FDE$ are right angles (Perpendicular lines intersect to form right angles)

(5) $\angle CBE \cong \angle FDE$ (All right angles are congruent.)

(6) $\overline{BC} \cong \overline{DF}$ (Given)

(7) $\triangle BCE \cong \triangle DFE$ (A.S.A)

(8) $\overline{CE} \cong \overline{FE}$ (C.P.C.T.C.)

(9) $\triangle CEF$ is isosceles (Definition of isosceles triangle)

Practice 78
a. 30
b. 0.7813
c. $y = 26$
d. $x = 6$
e. **(1)** $CDEF$ is a parallelogram (Given)
(2) $\overline{CD} \cong \overline{FE}$ and $\overline{CF} \cong \overline{DE}$ (Opposite sides of a parallelogram are congruent)
(3) $\overline{CD} \parallel \overline{FE}$ and $\overline{CF} \parallel \overline{DE}$ (Definition of parallelogram)
(4) $\angle CDH \cong \angle EFG$ and $\angle CFG \cong \angle EDH$ (Alternate interior angles are congruent)
(5) $\overline{FG} \cong \overline{DH}$ (Given)
(6) $\triangle DCH \cong \triangle FEG$ and $\triangle CFG \cong \triangle EDH$ (S.A.S.)
(7) $\overline{CH} \cong \overline{EG}$ and $\overline{CG} \cong \overline{EH}$ (C.P.C.T.C.)
(8) $CGEH$ is a parallelogram (If opposite sides of a quadrilateral are congruent, then it is a parallelogram.)

Problem Set 78
1. True
2. False

3. opposite, adjacent
4. perpendicular bisector
5. congruent
6. 720°
7. 1080°
8. $\overline{PR}$
9. $m\angle C = 102°$; $\overline{BE}$
10. $? = 7\sqrt{5}$
11. $? = 3\sqrt{21}$
12. 18
13. 42
14. 0.4040
15. 2.4751
16. $x = 17.32$
17. $y = 22.23$
18. $x = 45$
19. $y = 50$
20. $x = 9$
21. 12.21 feet
22. 2.55 miles
23. **(1)** $\dfrac{PS}{PT} = \dfrac{PR}{PQ}$ (Given)
(2) $\angle P \cong \angle P$ (Reflexive)
(3) $\triangle PSR \sim \triangle PTQ$ (S.A.S. Similarity)
(4) $\angle PSR \cong \angle T$ (C.P.C.T.C.)
(5) $\overline{SR} \parallel \overline{TQ}$ (If two lines form equal corresponding angles with a transversal, the lines are parallel.)
24. **(1)** $HIJK$ is a parallelogram (Given)
(2) $\overline{HI} \cong \overline{KJ}$ and $\overline{HK} \cong \overline{IJ}$ (Opposite sides of a parallelogram are congruent)

(3) $\overline{HI} \parallel \overline{KJ}$ and $\overline{HK} \parallel \overline{IJ}$ (Definition of parallelogram)
(4) $\angle LHI \cong \angle MJK$ and $\angle LHK \cong \angle MJI$ (Alternate interior angles are congruent)
(5) $\overline{HL} \cong \overline{JM}$ (Given)
(6) $\triangle HLI \cong \triangle JMK$ and $\triangle HLK \cong \triangle JMI$ (S.A.S.)
(7) $\overline{LK} \cong \overline{MI}$ and $\overline{MK} \cong \overline{LI}$ (C.P.C.T.C.)
(8) $LIMK$ is a parallelogram (If opposite sides of a quadrilateral are congruent, then it is a parallelogram)

Practice 79
a. $4\sqrt{13}$
b. $x = 44$
c. $y = 2\sqrt{22}$
d. 10.50 feet
e. **(1)** $\overline{AB}$ and $\overline{CD}$ bisect each other at point F. (Given)
(2) $\overline{AF} \cong \overline{FB}$ and $\overline{CF} \cong \overline{FD}$ (Definition of segment bisector)
(3) $\angle AFC \cong \angle BFD$ (Pairs of vertical angles are congruent.)
(4) $\triangle CAF \cong \triangle DBF$ (S.A.S.)

(5) $\angle C \cong \angle D$ and $\overline{CA} \cong \overline{BD}$
(C.P.C.T.C.)
(6) $\angle CAE \cong \angle GBD$
(Given)
(7) $\triangle CAE \cong \triangle DBG$
(A.S.A.)
(8) $\overline{AE} \cong \overline{GB}$
(C.P.C.T.C.)

Problem Set 79
1. True
2. True
3. adjacent, opposite
4. tan, sin, cos
5. diagonals
6. $6\sqrt{2}$; 8.46
7. $5\sqrt{7}$; 13.25
8. 0.3907
9. 0.2250
10. 6.3138
11. 52
12. $5\sqrt{17}$
13. In a proportion, the product of the means is equal to the product of the extremes.
14. Substitution Property of Inequality
15. $23\sqrt{2}$
16. $SM = 6$; $TM = 6\sqrt{3}$
17. $x = 8$
18. $y = 113$
19. $y = 4\sqrt{51}$
20. 31.89 ft.
21. 95.08 miles
22. 26.39 feet
23. **(1)** $ERDT$ is a trapezoid (Given)
(2) $\overline{RD} \parallel \overline{ET}$ (Definition of trapezoid)

(3) $\angle RDE \cong \angle TED$
(If two parallel lines are cut by a transversal, then their alternate interior angles are congruent.)
(4) $\angle RPD \cong \angle TPE$
(Pairs of vertical angles are congruent.)
(5) $\triangle RPD \sim \triangle TPE$
(A.A. Similarity)
(6) $\dfrac{DP}{EP} = \dfrac{RP}{TP}$
(Converse of definition of similar triangles)
(7) $DP \times TP = RP \times EP$ (In a proportion, the product of the means is equal to the product of the extremes.)

24. **(1)** $\overline{IJ}$ and $\overline{KL}$ bisect each other at point N. (Given)
(2) $\overline{IN} \cong \overline{NJ}$ and $\overline{KN} \cong \overline{NL}$
(Definition of segment bisector)
(3) $\angle INL \cong \angle JNK$
(Pairs of vertical angles are congruent.)
(4) $\triangle LIN \cong \triangle KJN$
(S.A.S.)
(5) $\angle K \cong \angle L$ and $\overline{LI} \cong \overline{JK}$
(C.P.C.T.C.)
(6) $\angle LIO \cong \angle MJK$
(Given)

(7) $\triangle LIO \cong \triangle KJM$
(A.S.A.)
(8) $\overline{IO} \cong \overline{MJ}$
(C.P.C.T.C.)

Practice 80
a. 30°, 60°, 90°
b. 19.64
c. $x = 55$
d. 28.97 feet
e. **(1)** $\overline{PQ} \cong \overline{PT}$; $\overline{OQ} \cong \overline{OT}$ (Given)
(2) $\overline{OP} \cong \overline{OP}$
(Reflexive)
(3) $\triangle OPQ \cong \triangle OPT$
(S.S.S.)
(4) $\angle OQP \cong \angle OTP$, (C.P.C.T.C.)
(5) $\angle OQP$ and $\angle RQO$ are supplementary; $\angle OTP$ and $\angle STO$ are supplementary. (If two angles are a linear pair, then they are supplementary.)
(6) $\angle RQO \cong \angle STO$
(If two angles are supplementary to congruent angles, then they are congruent.)
(7) $\angle ROQ \cong \angle SOT$
(Pairs of vertical angles are congruent.)
(8) $\triangle ROQ \cong \triangle SOT$
(A.S.A.)
(9) $\overline{RO} \cong \overline{SO}$
(C.P.C.T.C.)

(10) $\triangle RSO$ is isosceles. (Definition of isosceles triangle.)

Problem Set 80

1. True
2. True
3. parallel
4. not congruent, greater, longer
5. greater than
6. always
7. never
8. $\dfrac{UV}{UW}$
9. $\dfrac{VW}{UV}$
10. $98°$, $41°$, $41°$
11. $90°$, $60°$, $30°$
12. 0.75
13. 0.80
14. 40.95
15. 29.05
16. $? = 6$; $x = 11.25$
17. $? = 15$; $x = 11.25$
18. $x = 5\sqrt{2}$
19. $x = 84$
20. 16.30
21. 15.62 feet
22. 14.85 feet
23. **(1)** $\ell \parallel m$ (Given)

(2) $\angle ACB \cong \angle CBE$ (If two parallel lines are cut by a transversal, then their alternate interior angles are congruent.)

(3) $\overline{CB}$ bisects $\angle ABE$ (Given)

(4) $\angle ABC \cong \angle CBE$ (Definition of angle bisector)

(5) $\angle ACB \cong \angle ABC$ (Transitive)

(6) $\overline{AB} \cong \overline{AC}$ (Converse of Base Angles Theorem)

(7) D is the midpoint of $\overline{CB}$. (Given)

(8) $\overline{CD} \cong \overline{DB}$ (Definition of midpoint)

(9) $\triangle ADC \cong \triangle ADB$ (S.A.S.)

(10) $\angle BAD \cong \angle DAC$ (C.P.C.T.C.)

(11) $\overline{AD}$ bisects $\angle BAC$. (Definition of angle bisector)

24. **(1)** $\overline{KH} \cong \overline{LH}$; $\overline{JK} \cong \overline{JL}$ (Given)

(2) $\overline{JH} \cong \overline{JH}$ (Reflexive)

(3) $\triangle JKH \cong \triangle JLH$ (S.S.S.)

(4) $\angle JKH \cong \angle JLH$, (C.P.C.T.C.)

(5) $\angle JKH$ and $\angle FKJ$ are supplementary; $\angle JLH$ and $\angle GLJ$ are supplementary. (If two angles are a linear pair, then they are supplementary.)

(6) $\angle FKJ \cong \angle GLJ$ (If two angles are supplementary to congruent angles, then they are congruent.)

(7) $\angle FJK \cong \angle GJL$ (Pairs of vertical angles are congruent.)

(8) $\triangle FJK \cong \triangle GJL$ (A.S.A.)

(9) $\overline{FJ} \cong \overline{GJ}$ (C.P.C.T.C.)

(10) $\triangle FGJ$ is isosceles. (Definition of isosceles triangle.)

CHAPTER 12

Practice 81

a. $1\frac{1}{2}$ or $\frac{3}{2}$ inches

b. $x = 8$

c. $\tan x = 1$

d. 156 cars

e. **(1)** $\triangle MNO \cong \triangle QPO$
(Given)
(2) $\overline{NO} \cong \overline{PO}$ and $\overline{MN} \cong \overline{QP}$, or $NO = PO$ and $MN = QP$
(C.P.C.T.C.)
(3) $LM = LQ$
(Given)
(4) $LM + MN = LQ + QP$ (Addition Property)
(5) $LN = LM + MN$ and $LP = LQ + QP$ (Betweenness of Points)
(6) $LN = LP$, or $\overline{LN} \cong \overline{LP}$ (Substitution)
(7) $\overline{LO} \cong \overline{LO}$ (Reflexive)
(8) $\triangle LNO \cong \triangle LPO$ (S.S.S.)

Problem Set 81

1. True
2. True
3. chord
4. tangent; point of tangency
5. diameter
6. Parallelogram
7. Quadrilateral
8. 0.9703
9. 0.9703
10. $21\sqrt{2}$
11. $1\frac{1}{3}$ or $\frac{4}{3}$ inches
12. $\frac{14}{\sqrt{2}}$ or $7\sqrt{2}$ (fully simplified)
13. $JL = 13$; $KL = 13\sqrt{3}$
14. A.A.S.
15. None
16. $\angle F$
17. $m\angle D = 73$; DG is the longest side.
18. $x = 3$
19. $y = 67$
20. $\tan x = 1$
21. 95 lipstick wearers
22. 256 cars
23. **(1)** $\dfrac{QT}{QW} = \dfrac{QS}{QV}$
(Given)
(2) $\angle SQT \cong \angle VQW$ (Reflexive)
(3) $\triangle SQT \sim \triangle VQW$ (S.A.S. Similarity)
(4) $\angle VWQ \cong \angle STQ$ (Converse of definition of similar triangles)
(5) $\angle STQ \cong \angle RPQ$ (Given)
(6) $\angle VWQ \cong \angle RPQ$ (Transitive or Substitution)
(7) $\overline{PR} \parallel \overline{VW}$ (If two lines form congruent alternate interior angles with a transversal, then the lines are parallel.)
24. **(1)** $\triangle BCF \cong \triangle BHG$ (Given)
(2) $\overline{BC} \cong \overline{BH}$ and $\overline{CF} \cong \overline{HG}$, or $BC = BH$ and $CF = HG$ (C.P.C.T.C.)
(3) $FE = GE$ (Given)
(4) $CF + FE = HG + GE$ (Addition Property)
(5) $CE = CF + FE$ and $HE = HG + GE$ (Betweenness of Points)
(6) $CE = HE$, or $\overline{CE} \cong \overline{HE}$ (Substitution)
(7) $\overline{BE} \cong \overline{BE}$ (Reflexive)
(8) $\triangle BCE \cong \triangle BHE$ (S.S.S.)

Practice 82

a. secant line
b. 10
c. 5.66
d. 2.79 ft.
e. **(1)** $\overline{NP} \perp \overline{LM}$ and $\overline{RP} \perp \overline{SQ}$ (Given)
(2) $\angle PNM$ and $\angle PRQ$ are right angles (Definition of perpendicular)
(3) Draw radii $\overline{PM}$ and $\overline{PQ}$; $\overline{PM} \cong \overline{PQ}$ (All radii of the same circle are congruent)
(4) $\overline{NP} \cong \overline{RP}$ (Given)
(5) $\triangle PNM \cong \triangle PRQ$ (Hypotenuse-Leg)

(6) $MN = QR$ (C.P.C.T.C.)

(7) $\overline{NP}$ bisects chord $\overline{LM}$ and $\overline{RP}$ bisects chord $\overline{QS}$ (If a line through the center of a circle is perpendicular to a chord, it also bisects the chord.)

(8) $MN = NL$ and $QR = RS$ (Definition of bisector)

(9) $NL = RS$ (Transitive or Substitution)

(10) $MN + NL = QR + RS$ (Addition Property)

(11) $ML = MN + NL$ and $QS = QR + RS$ (Betweenness of Points)

(12) $ML = QS$ or $\overline{ML} \cong \overline{QS}$ (Substitution)

Problem Set 82

1. True
2. True
3. secant
4. radius
5. parallel
6. chord
7. tangent line
8. radius
9. $\overline{SV}$; 3.63
10. $m\angle G = 75$; $\overline{KG}$
11. $y = 12.00$
12. $x = 21.63$
13. $CD = 9$; $DF = 9\sqrt{3}$
14. 20
15. 116
16. 92

17. If a line through the center of a circle is perpendicular to a chord, it also bisects the chord.

18. In the same circle, congruent chords are equidistant from the center of the circle.

19. $x = 5$
20. $y = 5\sqrt{7}$
21. 6.63
22. 187 feet
23. 4.41 feet
24. **(1)** $\overline{QT} \perp \overline{PR}$ and $\overline{RU} \perp \overline{TS}$ (Given)

(2) $\angle TQP$ and $\angle RUS$ are right angles (Definition of perpendicular)

(3) $\angle TQP \cong \angle RUS$ (All right angles are congruent)

(4) $PRST$ is a parallelogram (Given)

(5) $\angle TPQ \cong \angle RSU$ (Opposite angles of a parallelogram are congruent.)

(6) $\overline{PT} \cong \overline{SR}$ (Opposite sides of a parallelogram are congruent)

(7) $\triangle PTQ \cong \triangle SRU$ (A.A.S.)

(8) $\overline{PQ} \cong \overline{SU}$ (C.P.C.T.C.)

25. **(1)** $\overline{AB} \perp \overline{FO}$ and $\overline{CD} \perp \overline{EO}$ (Given)

(2) $\angle AFO$ and $\angle OEC$ are right angles (Definition of perpendicular)

(3) Draw radii $\overline{AO}$ and $\overline{CO}$; $\overline{AO} \cong \overline{CO}$ (All radii of the same circle are congruent)

(4) $\overline{FO} \cong \overline{EO}$ (Given)

(5) $\triangle AFO \cong \triangle CEO$ (Hypotenuse-Leg)

(6) $AF = CE$ (C.P.C.T.C.)

(7) $\overline{FO}$ bisects chord $\overline{AB}$ and $\overline{EO}$ bisects chord $\overline{CD}$ (If a line through the center of a circle is perpendicular to a chord, it also bisects the chord.))

(8) $AF = FB$ and $CE = ED$ (Definition of bisector)

(9) $FB = ED$ (Transitive or Substitution)

(10) $AF + FB = CE + ED$ (Addition Property)

(11) $AB = AF + FB$ and $CD = CE + ED$ (Betweenness of Points)

(12) $AB = CD$ or $\overline{AB} \cong \overline{CD}$ (Substitution)

Practice 83

a. $? = 6.25$; $x = 11.79$
b. $RS = 25$
c. $9\sqrt{2}$
d. $m\angle H = 73$, $FG = 44$
e. $\overline{KL} \perp \overleftrightarrow{LW}$ at point L (Given). Assume $\overleftrightarrow{LW}$ is not a tangent

to ⊙K. That means it must intersect ⊙K at another point, W. Since $\overline{KW}$ is the hypotenuse of $\triangle KLW$, $KW > KL$. But if W is on the circle, KW should be a radius and equal to KL. The assumption that $\overleftrightarrow{LW}$ is not a tangent must be false. Therefore, $\overleftrightarrow{LW}$ has to be a tangent.

Problem Set 83

1. True
2. False
3. tangent segments
4. chords
5. similar
6. 7.42
7. ? $= 9.63$; $x = 11.91$
8. ? $= 3.58$; $x = 9.34$
9. $\overleftrightarrow{AB}$ and $\overleftrightarrow{CD}$
10. $\overleftrightarrow{FD}$ and $\overleftrightarrow{CG}$
11. 45°, 45°, 90°
12. 30°, 30°, 120°
13. $\overline{GH}$
14. $BN = 4$
15. 204
16. $IJ = 15$
17. If a radius is drawn to the point of tangency of a tangent line, then the radius is perpendicular to the tangent line.
18. If two tangent segments are drawn to a circle from the same exterior point, then they are congruent.

19. $x = 100$
20. $y = 72$
21. $x = 12\sqrt{2}$
22. 63, 27
23. $m\angle S = 116$, $PT = 42$
24. **(1)** Rectangle $ABCD$ and ⊙P (Given)
   (2) $\angle PCD$ is a right angle (Definition of rectangle)
   (3) $\overline{PC} \perp \overleftrightarrow{DC}$ (Definition of perpendicular lines)
   (4) $\overleftrightarrow{DC}$ is tangent to ⊙P. (If a radius is perpendicular to a line at the point where the line intersects a circle, then the line is a tangent line.)
25. $\overline{OP} \perp \overleftrightarrow{RP}$ at point P (Given). Assume $\overleftrightarrow{RP}$ is not a tangent to ⊙O. That means it must intersect ⊙O at another point, R. Since $\overline{OR}$ is the hypotenuse of $\triangle OPR$, $OR > OP$. But if R is on the circle, OR should be a radius and equal to OP. The assumption that $\overleftrightarrow{RP}$ is not a tangent must be false. Therefore, $\overleftrightarrow{RP}$ has to be a tangent.

Practice 84
   a. 55°

   b. base = 8.9, legs = 10.9
   c. $5\sqrt{6}$
   d. 30.47 feet
   e. **(1)** $\overline{JM} \cong \overline{IJ}$ (Given)
   (2) $\angle IMJ \cong \angle JIK$ (Base Angles Theorem)
   (3) $\angle IMJ \cong \angle LMK$ (Pairs of vertical angles are congruent.)
   (4) $\angle JIK \cong \angle LMK$ (Transitive)
   (5) $\overrightarrow{MK}$ bisects $\angle JKL$ (Given)
   (6) $\angle JKI \cong \angle MKL$ (Definition of angle bisector)
   (7) $\triangle KML \sim \triangle KIJ$ (A.A. Similarity)
   (8) $\dfrac{KI}{KM} = \dfrac{IJ}{ML}$ (Converse of definition of similar triangles)
   (9) $KI \times ML = KM \times IJ$ (In a proportion, the product of the means is equal to the product of the extremes.)

Problem Set 84
1. False
2. True
3. central angle
4. major arc, minor arc
5. tangent line
6. Regular pentagon; 108°
7. Regular decagon; 144°

8. 35°
9. 30°
10. 0.4961
11. 6.7
12. $HJ = 5\sqrt{3}$
13. base = 18.88, legs = 16.89
14. 24
15. 42.69
16. $x = 6\sqrt{6}$
17. $y = 12$
18. $x = 9$
19. S.A.S. Similarity
20. A.A. Similarity
21. 13.01 inches
22. 59.64 feet
23. **(1)** $\overrightarrow{JK}$ is tangent to $\odot P$ at J and to $\odot O$ at K. (Given)
(2) $\overline{PJ} \perp \overline{JK}$ and $\overline{KO} \perp \overline{JK}$ (If a radius is drawn to the point of tangency of a tangent line, then the radius is perpendicular to the tangent line.)
(3) $\angle PJK$ and $\angle OKM$ are right angles. (Perpendicular lines intersect to form right angles.)
(4) $\angle PJK \cong \angle OKM$ (All right angles are congruent.)
(5) $\overline{PJ} \parallel \overline{KO}$ (If two lines form congruent alternate exterior angles with a transversal, then the lines are parallel.)

(6) $\angle 1 \cong \angle 2$ (If two parallel lines are cut by a transversal, then their alternate interior angles are congruent.)
24. **(1)** $\overline{BE} \cong \overline{AB}$ (Given)
(2) $\angle AEB \cong \angle BAC$ (Base Angles Theorem)
(3) $\angle AEB \cong \angle DEC$ (Pairs of vertical angles are congruent.)
(4) $\angle BAC \cong \angle DEC$ (Transitive)
(5) $\overline{EC}$ bisects $\angle BCD$ (Given)
(6) $\angle BCA \cong \angle ECD$ (Definition of angle bisector)
(7) $\triangle CED \sim \triangle CAB$ (A.A. Similarity)
(8) $\dfrac{CA}{CE} = \dfrac{AB}{ED}$ (Converse of definition of similar triangles)
(9) $CA \times ED = CE \times AB$ (In a proportion, the product of the means is equal to the product of the extremes.)

Practice 85

a. $m\widehat{SP} = 97$
b. 44π
c. $XZ = 16$
d. $y = 2.98$

e. **(1)** $\overline{SP}$ is tangent to $\odot O$ at S and $\overline{RQ}$ is tangent to $\odot O$ at R (Given)
(2) $\angle PRQ$ and $\angle PSO$ are right angles (A radius drawn to tangent point is perpendicular to tangent line.)
(3) $\angle PRQ \cong \angle PSO$ (All right angles are congruent.)
(4) $\angle P \cong \angle P$ (Reflexive)
(5) $\triangle QRP \sim \triangle OSP$ (A. A. Similarity)

Problem Set 85

1. True
2. True
3. $\dfrac{\text{Arc length}}{\text{Circum.}} = \dfrac{\text{Degree meas.}}{360°}$
4. arc
5. central angle
6. $m\widehat{GD} = 120$
7. $m\angle COF = 154$
8. $m\widehat{CD} = 129$
9. $\dfrac{4\pi}{3}$
10. 20π
11. 23π
12. $3\sqrt{2}$
13. $9\sqrt{3}$
14. $DF = 20$
15. $m\angle J = 29$, $m\angle H = 63$, $m\angle N = 88$
16. $x = 25$
17. $y = 20$

18. $y = 4.61$

19. If a radius is perpendicular to a line at the point where the line intersects the circle, then the line is a tangent line.

20. In the same circle, chords equidistant from the center of the circle are congruent.

21. 132 oarfish

22. 187 points

23. **(1)** $\overline{HJ} \perp \overline{JK}$ and $\overline{JL} \perp \overline{HK}$ (Given)
(2) $\angle HJK$ is a right angle (Definition of perpendicular)
(3) JL is an altitude of $\triangle HJK$ (Definition of altitude)
(4) $\triangle HJK \sim \triangle HLJ$ (The altitude to the hypotenuse of a right triangle forms two triangles that are similar to each other and to the original triangle.)
(5) $\dfrac{HL}{HJ} = \dfrac{HJ}{HK}$ (Converse of definition of similar triangles)
(6) $HL \times HK = (HJ)^2$ (Cross-multiplication)
(7) $(HJ)^2 + (JK)^2 = (HK)^2$ (Pythagorean Theorem)

(8) $(HJ)^2 = (HK)^2 - (JK)^2$ (Subtraction property)
(9) $(HK)^2 - (JK)^2 = HL \times HK$ (Substitution)

24. **(1)** $\overline{DH}$ is tangent to $\odot O$ at D and $\overline{FG}$ is tangent to $\odot O$ at F (Given)
(2) $\angle HFG$ and $\angle HDO$ are right angles (A radius drawn to tangent point is perpendicular to tangent line.)
(3) $\angle HFG \cong \angle HDO$ (All right angles are congruent.)
(4) $\angle H \cong \angle H$ (Reflexive)
(5) $\triangle GFH \sim \triangle ODH$ (A. A. Similarity)

Practice 86

a. $m\widehat{HIF} = 203$

b. 7.57

c. 15.39

d. 1.78 miles

e. **(1)** Draw radii $\overline{OP}$ and $\overline{OR}$. (Two points determine a line.)
(2) $\overline{OP} \cong \overline{OR}$ (All radii of the same circle are congruent.)
(3) $\overline{QS} \perp \overline{PR}$ (Given)
(4) $\angle OTP$ and $\angle OTR$ are right angles. (Perpendicular lines

intersect to form right angles.)
(5) $\triangle OTP$ and $\triangle OTR$ are right triangles. (Definition of right triangle)
(6) $\overline{OT} \cong \overline{OT}$ (Reflexive)
(7) $\triangle OTP \cong \triangle OTR$ (Hypotenuse-Leg)
(8) $\angle POQ \cong \angle ROQ$ (C.P.C.T.C.)
(9) $m\angle POQ = m\widehat{PQ}$ and $m\angle ROQ = m\widehat{RQ}$ (The degree measure of a minor arc is the measure of its central angle.)
(10) $\widehat{PQ} \cong \widehat{RQ}$ (Substitution)

Problem Set 86

1. True
2. False
3. chords; congruent
4. perpendicular
5. chords
6. chord
7. secant
8. $m\angle BOC = 109$
9. $m\widehat{CDA} = 199$
10. 11.15
11. 35.88
12. 4.90
13. 9.38
14. $CE = 48$; $RS = 21$
15. 119
16. 35.21
17. 58.33
18. $x = 104$
19. $x = 15\sqrt{3}$
20. 36.93
21. 171.92 feet

22. 2.92 miles

23. (1) $OP > PR$ (Given)

(2) $m\angle ORP > m\angle POR$ (If unequal sides, then unequal angles.)

(3) $m\angle QOR > m\angle ORP$ (Exterior angle inequality)

(4) $m\angle QOR > m\angle POR$ (Transitive property of inequality)

(5) $m\angle QOR = m\overarc{QR}$ and $m\angle POR = m\overarc{PR}$ (The degree measure of a minor arc is the measure of its central angle.)

(6) $m\overarc{QR} > m\overarc{PR}$ (Substitution)

24. (1) Draw radii $\overline{OK}$ and $\overline{OL}$. (Two points determine a line.)

(2) $\overline{OK} \cong \overline{OL}$ (All radii of the same circle are congruent.)

(3) $\overline{IJ} \perp \overline{KL}$ (Given)

(4) $\angle ONK$ and $\angle ONL$ are right angles (Perpendicular lines intersect to form right angles.)

(5) ΔONK and ΔONL are right triangles. (Definition of right triangle)

(6) $\overline{ON} \cong \overline{ON}$ (Reflexive)

(7) $\Delta ONK \cong \Delta ONL$ (Hypotenuse-Leg)

(8) $\angle KOI \cong \angle LOI$ (C.P.C.T.C.)

(9) $m\angle KOI = m\overarc{KI}$ and $m\angle LOI = m\overarc{IL}$ (The degree measure of a minor arc is the measure of its central angle.)

(10) $\overarc{KI} \cong \overarc{IL}$ (Substitution)

Practice 87

a. $m\overarc{EG} = 24$

b. 94.2

c. $8\sqrt{3}$

d. 57

e. (1) $m\overarc{IJK} = m\overarc{LKJ}$ (Given)

(2) $m\overarc{IJ} + m\overarc{JK} = m\overarc{IJK}$ and $m\overarc{JK} + m\overarc{KL} = m\overarc{LKJ}$ (Arc Addition Postulate)

(3) $m\overarc{IJ} + m\overarc{JK} = m\overarc{JK} + m\overarc{KL}$ (Substitution)

(4) $m\overarc{IJ} = m\overarc{KL}$ (Subtraction)

(5) $m\angle IKJ = m\angle LJK$ (Inscribed angles that intersect congruent arcs are congruent.)

Problem Set 87

1. True
2. False
3. congruent
4. minor arcs; congruent
5. secant
6. $m\overarc{ADC} = 235$

7. $m\angle KLR = 40$
8. $m\overarc{PL} = 30$
9. 47.57
10. 135.02
11. $20\sqrt{3}$
12. 22
13. $\overline{KN}$
14. $DE = 39$
15. An inscribed angle that intercepts a semicircle is a right angle.
16. The measure of an angle formed by a tangent and a chord drawn to the point of tangency is equal to one-half the measure of the intercepted arc.
17. $x = 57.5$
18. $y = 130$
19. $x = 30$
20. $x = 73$
21. 66, 18
22. $m\angle H = 103$; $JG = 48$
23. (1) $m\overarc{ABC} = m\overarc{DCB}$ (Given)

(2) $m\overarc{AB} + m\overarc{BC} = m\overarc{ABC}$ and $m\overarc{DC} + m\overarc{CB} = m\overarc{DCB}$ (Arc Addition Postulate)

(3) $m\overarc{AB} + m\overarc{BC} = m\overarc{BC} + m\overarc{CD}$ (Substitution)

(4) $m\overarc{AB} = m\overarc{CD}$ (Subtraction)

(5) $m\angle ACB = m\angle DBC$ (Inscribed angles that intersect

congruent arcs are congruent.)

24. **(2)** If a radius is drawn to the point of tangency of a tangent line, then the radius is perpendicular to the tangent line.
(7) Arc Addition Postulate
(9) Multiplication
(10) An inscribed angle is equal in measure to one-half the measure of its intercepted arc.
(11) Substitution
(12) Subtraction
(13) Betweenness of Rays
(14) Subtraction
(15) Substitution

Practice 88

a. 4
b. $m\angle QPR = 66$
c. $x = 137.5$
d. $z = 90$
e. **(1)** $\overline{QS} \perp \overline{PR}$ (Given)
(2) $\overline{PS} \cong \overline{RS}$ (If a line through the center of a circle is perpendicular to a chord, it also bisects the chord.)
(3) $\overline{OS} \cong \overline{OS}$ (Reflexive)
(4) $\overline{OP} \cong \overline{OR}$ (All radii of the same circle are congruent.)
(5) $\triangle PSO \cong \triangle RSO$ (S.S.S.)

(6) $\angle POS \cong \angle ROS$ (C.P.C.T.C.)
(7) $\angle POQ$ is supplementary to $\angle POS$ and $\angle ROQ$ is supplementary to $\angle ROS$ (If two angles are a linear pair, then they are supplementary.)
(8) $\angle POQ \cong \angle ROQ$ (Angles supplementary to congruent angles are congruent.)
(9) $m\overset{\frown}{RQ} = m\overset{\frown}{PQ}$ (The degree measure of a minor arc is the measure of its central angle.)

Problem Set 88

1. True
2. True
3. semicircle
4. perpendicular
5. one-half
6. 152°
7. 76°
8. 18:19
9. 21:11
10. $m\angle U = 106$
11. $\sqrt{6}$
12. $m\angle APB = 65$
13. $m\angle JPH = 48$
14. 43
15. 68
16. The measure of an angle formed by two chords (or secants) intersecting in the interior of a circle is equal to one-half the sum of the measures

of the two intercepted arcs.

17. The measure of an angle formed by two secants (or tangents) intersecting in the exterior of a circle is equal to one-half the difference of the measures of the two intercepted arcs.
18. $d = 63$
19. $s = 80$
20. $x = 140$
21. $z = 80$
22. 5.41 feet
23. 0.39 miles
24. **(1)** $m\overset{\frown}{AE} + m\overset{\frown}{DC} = 180$ (Given)
(2) $m\angle ABE = \frac{1}{2}(m\overset{\frown}{AE} + m\overset{\frown}{DC})$ (The measure of an angle formed by two chords intersecting in the interior of a circle is equal to one-half the sum of the measures of the two intercepted arcs.)
(3) $m\angle ABE = \frac{1}{2}(180) = 90$ (Substitution)
(4) $m\angle ABE$ is a right angle. (Definition of right angle)
(5) $\overline{AC} \perp \overline{DE}$ (Perpendicular lines intersect to form right angles.)
25. **(1)** $\overline{BE} \perp \overline{AC}$ (Given)

(2) $\overline{AE} \cong \overline{CE}$ (If a line through the center of a circle is perpendicular to a chord, it also bisects the chord.)

(3) $\overline{EO} \cong \overline{EO}$ (Reflexive)

(4) $\overline{OA} \cong \overline{OC}$ (All radii of the same circle are congruent.)

(5) $\triangle AEO \cong \triangle CEO$ (S.S.S.)

(6) $\angle AOE \cong \angle COE$ (C.P.C.T.C.)

(7) $\angle AOB$ is supplementary to $\angle AOE$ and $\angle COB$ is supplementary to $\angle COE$ (If two angles are a linear pair, then they are supplementary.)

(8) $\angle AOB \cong \angle COB$ (Angles supplementary to congruent angles are congruent.)

(9) $m\overset{\frown}{CB} = m\overset{\frown}{AB}$ (The degree measure of a minor arc is the measure of its central angle.)

Practice 89

a. $m\overset{\frown}{SQ} = 60$

b. 90π

c. $b = 130$

d. $DE = 6$

e. **(1)** $m\overset{\frown}{MI} = 2m\overset{\frown}{LJ}$ (Given)

(2) $m\angle MKI = \frac{1}{2}(m\overset{\frown}{MI} - m\overset{\frown}{LJ})$ (The measure of an angle formed by two secants intersecting in the exterior of a circle is equal to one-half the difference of the measures of the two intercepted arcs.)

(3) $m\angle MKI = \frac{1}{2}(2m\overset{\frown}{LJ} - m\overset{\frown}{LJ})$ or $m\angle MKI = \frac{1}{2}(m\overset{\frown}{LJ})$ (Substitution)

(4) $m\angle KMJ = \frac{1}{2}m\overset{\frown}{LJ}$ (An inscribed angle is equal in measure to one-half the measure of its intercepted arc.)

(5) $m\angle MKI = m\angle KMJ$ (Transitive)

(6) $KJ = MJ$ (Converse of Base Angles Theorem)

(7) $\triangle MJK$ is isosceles (Definition of isosceles triangle)

Problem Set 89

1. False
2. False
3. tangent segment, secant segment, tangent segment, secant segment
4. sum
5. difference
6. $m\overset{\frown}{KL} = 115$
7. $m\angle JOL = 160$
8. $m\overset{\frown}{BD} = 52$
9. 8π meters
10. 128π
11. 26
12. $\sqrt{2}$
13. 27
14. 3
15. 9
16. 12
17. $h = 10$
18. $b = 132.5$
19. $x = 3$
20. $k = 59$
21. 63 chocolate bunnies
22. 114 turnip trucks
23. **(1)** $\overline{AC}$ and $\overline{AE}$ are secant segments (Given)

    (2) $AC \times AB = AE \times AD$ (If two secant segments are drawn to a circle from the same exterior point, then the product of the lengths of one secant segment and its external segment is equal to the product of the lengths of the other secant segment and its external segment)

    (3) $AC = AE$ (Given)

    (4) $AE \times AB = AE \times AD$ (Substitution)

    (5) $AB = AD$ (Division)

24. **(1)** $m\overset{\frown}{PT} = 2m\overset{\frown}{QS}$ (Given)

(2) $m\angle PRT =$
$\frac{1}{2}(m\widehat{PT} - m\widehat{QS})$
(The measure of an angle formed by two secants intersecting in the exterior of a circle is equal to one-half the difference of the measures of the two intercepted arcs.)

(3) $m\angle PRT =$
$\frac{1}{2}(2m\widehat{QS} - m\widehat{QS})$ or
$m\angle PRT = \frac{1}{2}(m\widehat{QS})$
(Substitution)

(4) $m\angle RPS =$
$\frac{1}{2}m\widehat{QS}$ (An inscribed angle is equal in measure to one-half the measure of its intercepted arc.)

(5) $m\angle PRT =$
$m\angle RPS$ (Transitive)

(6) $RS = PS$
(Converse of Base Angles Theorem)

(7) $\triangle RSP$ is isosceles (Definition of isosceles triangle)

CHAPTER 13

Practice 90

a. 48 ft.^2
b. $\angle C$
c. 18.9 in.
d. $x = 70$
e. (1) $m\overset{\frown}{EF} = m\overset{\frown}{GH}$ (Given)
(2) $\overline{EF} \cong \overline{GH}$ (If two minor arcs of the same circle are congruent, then their intersecting chords are congruent.)
(3) $\overline{OE} \cong \overline{OH}$ and $\overline{OF} \cong \overline{OG}$ (All radii of the same circle are congruent.)
(4) $\triangle EOF \cong \triangle HOG$ (S.S.S.)
(5) $m\angle EFO = m\angle HGO$ (C.P.C.T.C.)
(6) $\triangle FGO$ is isosceles (Definition of isosceles triangle)
(7) $m\angle OFG = m\angle OGF$ (Base Angles Theorem)
(8) $m\angle EFO + m\angle OFG = m\angle HGO + m\angle OGF$ (Addition)
(9) $m\angle EFO + m\angle OFG = m\angle EFG$ and $m\angle HGO + m\angle OGF = m\angle FGH$ (Betweenness of Rays)
(10) $m\angle EFG = m\angle FGH$ (Substitution)

Problem Set 90

1. False
2. False
3. base; altitude
4. product, product
5. external segment, external segment
6. $32.5°$
7. $40°$
8. 72 sq. in.
9. 192 ft.^2
10. $\overline{JK}$
11. $\angle R$
12. 26
13. 20.2 in.
14. 72
15. $2a + 2d$
16. 3
17. 22
18. $a = 40$
19. $s = 22.5$
20. $x = 65$
21. $40, 16$
22. $FG = 22$, $GH = 33$, $HJ = 44$
23. (1) $OP > PR$ (Given)
(2) $m\angle ORP > m\angle POR$ (If unequal sides, then unequal angles.)
(3) $m\angle QOR > m\angle ORP$ (Exterior Angle Inequality)
(4) $m\angle QOR > m\angle POR$ (Transitive property of inequality)
(5) $m\angle QOR = m\overset{\frown}{QR}$ and $m\angle POR = m\overset{\frown}{PR}$ (The degree measure of a minor arc is the measure of its central angle.)
(6) $m\overset{\frown}{QR} > m\overset{\frown}{PR}$ (Substitution)

24. (1) $m\overset{\frown}{IJ} = m\overset{\frown}{KL}$ (Given)
(2) $\overline{IJ} \cong \overline{KL}$ (If two minor arcs of the same circle are congruent, then their intersecting chords are congruent.)
(3) $\overline{OI} \cong \overline{OL}$ and $\overline{OJ} \cong \overline{OK}$ (All radii of the same circle are congruent.)
(4) $\triangle IOJ \cong \triangle LOK$ (S.S.S.)
(5) $m\angle IJO = m\angle LKO$ (C.P.C.T.C.)
(6) $\triangle JKO$ is isosceles. (Definition of isosceles triangle)
(7) $m\angle OJK = m\angle OKJ$ (Base Angles Theorem)
(8) $m\angle IJO + m\angle OJK = m\angle LKO + m\angle OKJ$ (Addition)
(9) $m\angle IJO + m\angle OJK = m\angle IJK$ and $m\angle LKO + m\angle OKJ = m\angle JKL$ (Betweenness of Rays)
(10) $m\angle IJK = m\angle JKL$ (Substitution)

Practice 91

a. 18
b. 144
c. 48

d. $AC = 6\sqrt{10}$

e. **(1)** $\overline{VT}$ is tangent to $\odot P$ at U; $\overline{RT}$ is tangent to $\odot P$ at S; $\overline{VR}$ is tangent to $\odot P$ at W. (Given)
(2) $VU = VW$, $UT = TS$, and $WR = SR$ (If two tangent segments are drawn to a circle from the same exterior point, then they are congruent (equal).)
(3) $TS = SR$ (Given)
(4) $UT = SR$ (Transitive or substitution)
(5) $UT = WR$ (Transitive or substitution)
(6) $VU + UT = VW + WR$ (Addition)
(7) $VU + UT = VT$ and $VW + WR = VR$ (Betweenness of Points)
(8) $VT = VR$ (Substitution)
(9) $\triangle VTR$ is isosceles. (Definition of isosceles triangle)
(10) $\angle T \cong \angle R$ (Base Angles Theorem)

Problem Set 91
1. True
2. True
3. Equivalent
4. sum
5. inscribed angle
6. 46.89 inches
7. 75.10
8. 30
9. 9

10. 72
11. $m\angle D = 60$, $m\angle E = 30$, $m\angle F = 90$
12. 60
13. If two chords intersect in the interior of a circle, the product of the lengths of the segments of one chord is equal to the product of the lengths of the segments of the other.
14. If two secant segments are drawn to a circle from the same exterior point, then the product of the lengths of one secant segment and its external segment is equal to the product of the lengths of the other secant segment and its external segment.
15. $m\angle MNL = 73$
16. $m\angle RPT = 24$
17. $b = 88$
18. $y = 50$
19. $x = 6$
20. $QJ = 8\sqrt{5}$
21. 147.20 ft.
22. 51.58 ft.
23. **(1)** $\overline{DC} \cong \overline{AB}$ (Given)
(2) $m\widehat{DC} = m\widehat{AB}$ (If two chords of the same circle are congruent, then their minor arcs are congruent.)
(3) $m\widehat{DC} + m\widehat{BC} = m\widehat{AB} + m\widehat{BC}$ (Addition)
(4) $m\widehat{DC} + m\widehat{BC} = m\widehat{DB}$ and $m\widehat{AB} + m\widehat{BC} = m\widehat{AC}$ (Arc Addition Postulate)
(5) $m\widehat{DB} = m\widehat{AC}$ (Substitution)
(6) $\overline{DB} \cong \overline{AC}$ (If two minor arcs of the same circle are congruent, then their intersected chords are congruent.)

24. **(1)** $\overline{HF}$ is tangent to $\odot O$ at C, $\overline{GF}$ is tangent to $\odot O$ at D, and $\overline{HG}$ is tangent to $\odot O$ at E (Given)
(2) $HC = HE$, $CF = FD$, and $EG = DG$ (If two tangent segments are drawn to a circle from the same exterior point, then they are congruent (equal).)
(3) $FD = DG$ (Given)
(4) $CF = DG$ (Transitive or substitution)
(5) $CF = EG$ (Transitive or substitution)
(6) $HC + CF = HE + EG$ (Addition)
(7) $HC + CF = HF$ and $HE + EG = HG$ (Betweenness of Points)

(8) $HF = HG$
(Substitution)
(9) $\triangle HFG$ is
isosceles. (Definition
of isosceles triangle)
(10) $\angle F \cong \angle G$
(Base Angles
Theorem)

Practice 92
a. 330
b. 27
c. $a = 90$
d. $y = 11$
e. **(1)** $\overline{PR}$ is tangent to
$\odot O$ at P and $\overline{QR}$ is
tangent to $\odot O$ at Q
(Given)
(2) $\overline{PR} \cong \overline{QR}$ (If two
tangent segments are
drawn to a circle
from the same
exterior point, then
they are congruent.)
(3) $\angle RPO$ and
$\angle RQO$ are right
angles (If a radius is
drawn to the point of
tangency of a tangent
line, then the radius
is perpendicular to
the tangent line.)
(4) $\overline{RO} \cong \overline{RO}$
(Reflexive)
(5) $\triangle RPO \cong \triangle RQO$
(H.L.)
(6) $\angle PRO \cong \angle QRO$
(C.P.C.T.C.)
(7) $\overrightarrow{RS}$ bisects
$\angle PRQ$ (Definition
of an angle bisector.)

Problem Set 92
1. True
2. True
3. square
4. triangle
5. one-half
6. $m\overset{\frown}{LN} = 49$
7. $m\angle POL = 131$
8. 190
9. 145
10. 108
11. 120
12. 26
13. $DF = 156$
14. 42.76
15. 38.56
16. $FG = 7$
17. $HJ = 12$
18. $a = 81$
19. $x = 10$
20. $y = 34$
21. 54 nail biters
22. 357 monkeys
23. **(1)** $\overline{JL}$ is tangent to
$\odot P$ at K and to $\odot O$
at L; $\overline{JN}$ is tangent
to $\odot P$ at M and to
$\odot O$ at N (Given)
(2) $JL = JN$ (If two
tangent segments are
drawn to a circle
from the same
exterior point, then
they are congruent.)
(3) $JL = JK + KL$
and $JN = JM + MN$
(Betweenness of
Points)
(4) $JK + KL =$
$JM + MN$
(Substitution)
(5) $JK = JM$ (If two
tangent segments are
drawn to a circle

from the same
exterior point, then
they are congruent
(equal).)
(6) $JM + KL =$
$JM + MN$
(Substitution)
(7) $KL = MN$
(Subtraction)

24. **(1)** $\overline{BD}$ is tangent to
$\odot O$ at B and $\overline{CD}$ is
tangent to $\odot O$ at C
(Given)
(2) $\overline{BD} \cong \overline{CD}$ (If two
tangent segments are
drawn to a circle
from the same
exterior point, then
they are congruent.)
(3) $\angle DBO$ and
$\angle DCO$ are right
angles (If a radius is
drawn to the point of
tangency of a tangent
line, then the radius
is perpendicular to
the tangent line.)
(4) $\overline{DO} \cong \overline{DO}$
(Reflexive)
(5) $\triangle DBO \cong \triangle DCO$
(H.L.)
(6) $\angle BDO \cong \angle CDO$
(C.P.C.T.C.)
(7) $\overrightarrow{DE}$ bisects
$\angle BDC$ (Definition
of an angle bisector.)

Practice 93
a. $24\sqrt{3}$ sq. in.
b. 50°, 40°, 90°
c. 30
d. $y = 106$

e. Inscribe the regular polygon in $\odot O$. Draw radii of the regular polygon. Since the polygon is regular, all the sides are congruent. The sides are chords of the circle, so all the intercepted arcs are also congruent. Therefore, all the central angles are congruent.

Problem Set 93

1. False
2. False
3. central angle
4. apothem
5. rhombus
6. 612 cm^2
7. 240 sq. in.
8. 264 in.^{2}
9. 104 sq. ft.
10. $\overline{MN}$
11. $\angle T$
12. If two figures are congruent, then they have equal areas.
13. The area of a closed region is equal to the sum of the areas of the nonoverlapping parts. (Area Addition Postulate)
14. 45°, 45°, 90°
15. 55°, 35°, 90°
16. $m\angle DCF = 39$
17. $m\angle RPQ = 18$
18. 34
19. $x = 15$
20. $y = 25$
21. 400.57 ft.

22. 4.26 feet
23. Inscribe the regular polygon in $\odot P$. Draw radii of the regular polygon. Since the polygon is regular, all the sides are congruent. The sides are chords of the circle, so all the intercepted arcs are also congruent. Therefore, all the central angles are congruent.
24. **(1)** $OABC$ is a square (Given)
(2) $\overline{OA} \perp \overline{AB}$, $\overline{OC} \perp \overline{BC}$ and $OA = OC$ (Definition of a square)
(3) $MS = NR$ (In the same circle, chords equidistant from the center of the circle are equal)
(4) $m\widehat{MS} = m\widehat{NR}$ (If two chords of the same circle are congruent, then their minor arcs are congruent.)
(5) $m\widehat{MN} + m\widehat{NS} = m\widehat{MS}$ and $m\widehat{NS} + m\widehat{SR} = m\widehat{NR}$ (Arc Addition Postulate)
(6) $m\widehat{MN} + m\widehat{NS} = m\widehat{NS} + m\widehat{SR}$ (Substitution)
(7) $m\widehat{MN} = m\widehat{SR}$ (Subtraction)

Practice 94
a. $9\pi - 18$
b. $20 + 5\pi$ ft.
c. $y = 5$
d. 486
e. **(1)** $m\angle JLM = m\angle KLI$ (Given)
(2) $m\angle JLM = m\angle JLI + m\angle ILM$ and $m\angle KLI = m\angle KLJ + m\angle JLI$ (Betweenness of Rays)
(3) $m\angle JLI + m\angle ILM = m\angle KLJ + m\angle JLI$ (Substitution)
(4) $m\angle ILM = m\angle KLJ$ (Subtraction)
(5) $\overline{JL} \cong \overline{IL}$ and $\overline{KL} \cong \overline{ML}$ (Given)
(6) $\triangle JKL \cong \triangle ILM$ (S.A.S.)
(7) $\alpha\triangle JKL = \alpha\triangle ILM$ (If two figures are congruent, then they have equal areas.)
(8) $\alpha\triangle JKL + \alpha\triangle JLI = \alpha\triangle ILM + \alpha\triangle JLI$ (Addition)
(9) area of polygon $KLIJ$ = area of polygon $MLJI$ (Substitution)

Problem Set 94
1. True
2. True
3. $\dfrac{\text{Area of sector}}{\text{Area of circle}} = \dfrac{\text{Degree measure}}{360}$
4. square

5. center
6. 28π inches
7. 48π cm
8. 28π
9. 27π
10. $36\pi - 72$
11. 42 cm^2
12. 32 in.^{2}
13. 77 feet
14. 120
15. $12 + 3\pi$ ft.
16. 9
17. 20
18. $d = 17$
19. $n = 36$
20. $x = 4$
21. 384
22. 216
23. **(1)** Q is the midpoint of $\overset{\frown}{RQS}$. (Given)

(2) $m\overset{\frown}{RQ} = m\overset{\frown}{QS}$ (Definition of the midpoint of an arc)

(3) $\angle RPQ \cong \angle TPQ$ (Inscribed angles that intercept the same or congruent arcs are congruent.)

(4) $\overline{PQ}$ is a diameter of $\odot O$. (Given)

(5) $\overset{\frown}{QSP}$ is a semicircle. (Definition of a semicircle)

(6) $\angle QRP$ is a right angle. (An inscribed angle that intercepts a semicircle is a right angle.)

(7) $\overline{TQ}$ is a tangent to $\odot O$ at Q. (Given)

(8) $\overline{QT} \perp \overline{QO}$ (If a radius is drawn to the point of tangency of a tangent line, the radius is perpendicular to the tangent line.)

(9) $\angle TQP$ is a right angle. (Perpendicular lines are lines which intersect to form right angles.)

(10) $\angle QRP \cong \angle TQP$ (All right angles are congruent.)

(11) $\Delta QPT \sim \Delta QRP$ (A.A. Similarity)

24. **(1)** $m\angle SQP = m\angle TQR$ (Given)

(2) $m\angle SQP = m\angle SQR + m\angle RQP$ and $m\angle TQR = m\angle TQS + m\angle SQR$ (Betweenness of Rays)

(3) $m\angle SQR + m\angle RQP = m\angle TQS + m\angle SQR$ (Substitution)

(4) $m\angle RQP = m\angle TQS$ (Subtraction)

(5) $\overline{SQ} \cong \overline{RQ}$ and $\overline{TQ} \cong \overline{PQ}$ (Given)

(6) $\Delta STQ \cong \Delta RPQ$ (S.A.S.)

(7) $\alpha\Delta STQ = \alpha\Delta RPQ$ (If two figures are congruent, then they have equal areas.)

(8) $\alpha\Delta STQ + \alpha\Delta SQR = \alpha\Delta RPQ + \alpha\Delta SQR$ (Addition)

(9) area of polygon $TQRS$ = area of polygon $PQSR$ (Substitution)

CHAPTER 14

Practice 95
a. $120°$
b. 288
c. $96\pi - 144\sqrt{3}$
d. $y = 40$
e. **(1)** $\overline{QR}$ is a diameter of $\odot O$ (Given)
(2) $\angle RPQ$ and $\angle RSQ$ are right angles. (An inscribed angle that intercepts a semicircle is a right angle.)
(3) $\overline{PQ} \parallel \overline{AO}$ and $\overline{SQ} \parallel \overline{BO}$ (Given)
(4) $\angle RAO$ and $\angle RBO$ are right angles (If two parallel lines are cut by a transversal, then their corresponding angles are congruent.)
(5) $\overline{RA} \cong \overline{RB}$ (Given)
(6) $\overline{RO} \cong \overline{RO}$ (Reflexive)
(7) $\triangle RAO \cong \triangle RBO$ (Hypotenuse-Leg)
(8) $\overline{AO} \cong \overline{BO}$ (C.P.C.T.C.)
(9) $\overline{RP} \cong \overline{RS}$ (In the same circle, chords equidistant from the center of the circle are congruent.)

Problem Set 95
1. True
2. True
3. volume
4. surface area
5. length, width, altitude
6. $120°$
7. $300°$
8. 78
9. $256 + 32\pi$
10. 10π ft.^{2}
11. $24\pi - 36\sqrt{3}$
12. $8\sqrt{3}$
13. 240 sq. ft.
14. Area $= 104$ sq. in.; Vol. $= 60$ cu. in.
15. Area $= 426$ cm^2; Vol. $= 540$ cm^3
16. $48°, 96°, 36°$
17. $36°, 108°, 36°$
18. $x = 15$
19. $c = \dfrac{ab}{d}$
20. $x = 20$
21. 828 munchers
22. 180 foot stompers
23. **(1)** $\overline{AB}$ and $\overline{CB}$ are tangent segments to $\odot O$. (Given)
(2) $\overline{AB} \perp \overline{AO}$ and $\overline{CB} \perp \overline{CO}$ (If a radius is drawn to the point of tangency of a tangent line, the radius is perpendicular to the tangent line.)
(3) $\angle OAB$ and $\angle OCB$ are right angles. (Perpendicular lines intersect to form right angles.)
(4) $m\angle OAB = 90$ and $m\angle OCB = 90$ (Definition of right angle)
(5) $m\angle O + m\angle OAB + m\angle OCB + m\angle B = 360$ (The sum of the measures of the angles of a quadrilateral is 360.)
(6) $m\overset{\frown}{AC} = m\angle O$ (The degree measure of a minor arc is the measure of its central angle.)
(7) $m\overset{\frown}{AC} + 90 + 90 + m\angle B = 360$ (Substitution)
(8) $m\angle B = 180 - m\overset{\frown}{AC}$ (Subtraction)

24. **(1)** $\overline{FG}$ is a diameter of $\odot O$ (Given)
(2) $\angle GEF$ and $\angle GHF$ are right angles (An inscribed angle that intercepts a semicircle is a right angle.)
(3) $\overline{EF} \parallel \overline{JO}$ and $\overline{HF} \parallel \overline{KO}$ (Given)
(4) $\angle GJO$ and $\angle GKO$ are right angles. (If two parallel lines are cut by a transversal, then their corresponding angles are congruent.)
(5) $\overline{GJ} \cong \overline{GK}$ (Given)
(6) $\overline{GO} \cong \overline{GO}$ (Reflexive)
(7) $\triangle GJO \cong \triangle GKO$ (Hypotenuse-Leg)
(8) $\overline{JO} \cong \overline{KO}$ (C.P.C.T.C.)

(9) $\overline{GE} \cong \overline{GH}$ (In the same circle, chords equidistant from the center of the circle are congruent.)

Practice 96
a. 22.5π in.^{2}
b. 780
c. 1,500
d. $\dfrac{2}{3}\sqrt{3}$
e. **(1)** $\overline{EC}$ is a diameter of $\odot O$ (Given)
(2) $\angle EBC$ is a right angle. (An inscribed angle that intercepts a semicircle is a right angle.)
(3) $\overline{DE} \perp \overline{DB}$ (Given)
(4) $\angle BDE$ is a right angle. (Perpendicular lines intersect to form right angles.)
(5) $\angle EBC \cong \angle BDE$ (All right angles are congruent.)
(6) $\overline{DE}$ is tangent to $\odot O$ at E. (Given)
(7) $m\angle DEB = \dfrac{1}{2}m\widehat{EB}$ (The measure of an angle formed by a tangent and a chord drawn to the point of tangency is equal to one-half the measure of the intercepted arc.)
(8) $m\angle BCE = \dfrac{1}{2}m\widehat{EB}$ (An ins-

cribed angle is equal in measure to one-half the measure of its intercepted arc.)
(9) $m\angle DEB = m\angle BCE$ (Transitive or Substitution)
(10) $\triangle DEB \sim \triangle BCE$ (A.A. Similarity)
(11) $\dfrac{DB}{BE} = \dfrac{BE}{EC}$ (Converse of definition of similar triangles)

Problem Set 96
1. True
2. False
3. area of the base; altitude
4. rectangular solid
5. segment
6. 88 sq. in.
7. 27π
8. 48π in.^{2}
9. Triangular right prism
10. Quadrilateral oblique prism
11. Octagonal right prism
12. 304
13. 195
14. 105
15. 1,778
16. $14 + 6\pi$
17. 12π
18. 51
19. 32
20. $\dfrac{4}{3}\sqrt{3}$
21. $\dfrac{\pi}{2}$
22. $\sqrt{\pi}$

23. **(1)** $\widehat{AB} \cong \widehat{CD}$ (Given)
(2) $\overline{AB} \cong \overline{CD}$ (If two minor arcs of the same circle are congruent, then their intersecting chords are congruent.)
(3) $\overline{BC} \parallel \overline{AD}$ (Given)
(4) $ABCD$ is an isosceles trapezoid. (Definition of isosceles trapezoid)
(5) $\angle A \cong \angle D$ (Base angles of an isosceles trapezoid are congruent.)

24. **(1)** $\overline{LN}$ is a diameter of $\odot O$. (Given)
(2) $\angle LMN$ is a right angle. (An inscribed angle that intercepts a semicircle is a right angle.)
(3) $\overline{KL} \perp \overline{KM}$ (Given)
(4) $\angle MKL$ is a right angle. (Perpendicular lines intersect to form right angles.)
(5) $\angle LMN \cong \angle MKL$ (All right angles are congruent.)
(6) $\overline{KL}$ is tangent to $\odot O$ at L. (Given)
(7) $m\angle KLM = \dfrac{1}{2}m\widehat{LM}$ (The measure of an angle formed by a tangent and a chord drawn to the point of tangency is equal to one-half

the measure of the intercepted arc.)

(8) $m\angle MNL = \frac{1}{2}m\widehat{LM}$ (An ins-cribed angle is equal in measure to one-half the measure of its intercepted arc.)

(9) $m\angle KLM = m\angle MNL$ (Transitive or Substitution)

(10) $\triangle KLM \sim \triangle MNL$ (A.A. Similarity)

(11) $\frac{KM}{ML} = \frac{ML}{LN}$ (Converse of definition of similar triangles)

Practice 97

a. 30

b. 40

c. 150

d. $m = \dfrac{qp + p^2 - n^2}{n}$

e. **(1)** $ABCDEF$ is a regular polygon (Given)

(2) Draw $\overline{OA}$ and $\overline{OC}$ (Two points determine a line.)

(3) $\overline{AB} \cong \overline{BC}$ (Def-inition of a regular polygon)

(4) $\overline{OA} \cong \overline{OB}$ and $\overline{OB} \cong \overline{OC}$ (Defini-tion of radius of a regular polygon)

(5) $\triangle ABO \cong \triangle BCO$ (S.S.S.)

(6) $\angle BAO \cong \angle CBO$ (C.P.C.T.C.)

(7) $\triangle ABO$ and $\triangle BCO$ are isosceles. (Definition of isosceles triangles)

(8) $\angle ABO \cong \angle BAO$ (Base Angles Theorem)

(9) $\angle ABO \cong \angle CBO$ (Transitive)

(10) $\overline{OB}$ bisects $\angle ABC$ (Definition of angle bisector)

Problem Set 97

1. True
2. True
3. slant height
4. altitude; perimeter; area of a base
5. square
6. $144 - 36\pi$
7. $32 - 8\pi$
8. 348
9. 7.5
10. Rectangular solid
11. Pentagonal right prism
12. Triangular pyramid
13. 62
14. 133
15. 846
16. 324
17. 63
18. $a = 4$
19. $b = 72$
20. $s = \dfrac{uv + v^2 - t^2}{t}$
21. $DO = 9$
22. $AK = 24$
23. **(1)** $\overline{FG} \parallel \overline{DE}$ (Given)

(2) $m\angle FGD = m\angle EDG$ (If two parallel lines are cut by a transversal, then their alternate interior angles are equal.)

(3) $m\angle FGD = \frac{1}{2}m\widehat{DF}$ and $m\angle EDG = \frac{1}{2}m\widehat{GE}$ (An inscribed angle is equal in measure to one-half the measure of its intercepted arc.)

(4) $\frac{1}{2}m\widehat{DF} = \frac{1}{2}m\widehat{GE}$ (Substitution)

(5) $m\widehat{DF} = m\widehat{GE}$ (Multiplication)

(6) $\widehat{DF} \cong \widehat{EG}$ (Congruent arcs have equal measures.)

24. **(1)** $ABCDEFGH$ is a regular polygon (Given)

(2) Draw $\overline{OA}$ and $\overline{OC}$ (Two points determine a line.)

(3) $\overline{AB} \cong \overline{BC}$ (Definition of a regular polygon)

(4) $\overline{OA} \cong \overline{OB}$ and $\overline{OB} \cong \overline{OC}$ (Defini-tion of radius of a regular polygon)

(5) $\triangle ABO \cong \triangle BCO$ (S.S.S.)

(6) $\angle BAO \cong \angle CBO$ (C.P.C.T.C.)

(7) $\triangle ABO$ and $\triangle BCO$ are isosceles. (Definition of isosceles triangles)

(8) $\angle ABO \cong \angle BAO$ (Base Angles Theorem)
(9) $\angle ABO \cong \angle CBO$ (Transitive)
(10) $\overline{OB}$ bisects $\angle ABC$ (Definition of angle bisector)

Practice 98
a. 45
b. 119
c. 36π
d. 20
e. **(1)** $QRSTUVWX$ is a regular polygon. (Given)
(2) $\angle OPX$ and $\angle OPW$ are right angles. (Definition of apothem of a regular polygon)
(3) $\overline{OX} \cong \overline{OW}$ (Definition of radius of a regular polygon)
(4) $\overline{OP} \cong \overline{OP}$ (Reflexive)
(5) $\triangle XPO \cong \triangle WPO$ (H.L.)
(6) $\angle XOP \cong \angle WOP$ (C.P.C.T.C.)
(7) $\overline{OP}$ bisects $\angle XOW$. (Definition of angle bisector)

Problem Set 98
1. True
2. True
3. $\pi r^2 a$
4. $\dfrac{1}{3}\pi r^2 a$
5. altitude; perimeter; base

6. 40
7. 32
8. $264 - 18\pi$
9. 375
10. 184
11. 42 cubic in.
12. $1,472\pi$
13. 180π
14. 64
15. 80
16. 115
17. 43
18. 8
19. 72
20. 10
21. 3.58 ft.
22. 14.91 ft
23. **(1)** $\overline{BC}$ is tangent to $\odot O$ at B. (Given)
(2) $\angle ABC$ is a right angle. (If a radius is drawn to the point of tangency, the radius is perpendicular to tangent line.)
(3) $\overline{AB}$ is a diameter of $\odot O$. (Given)
(4) $\angle ADB$ is a right angle. (An inscribed angle that intercepts a semicircle is a right angle.)
(5) $\overline{BD}$ is an altitude of right $\triangle ABC$. (Definition of altitude)
(6) $\triangle ABC \sim \triangle ADB \sim \triangle BDC$ (The altitude to hypotenuse of right triangle forms two triangles similar to each other and to original triangle.)

24. **(1)** $ABCDEF$ is a regular polygon. (Given)
(2) $\angle OPB$ and $\angle OPC$ are right angles. (Definition of apothem of a regular polygon)
(3) $\overline{OB} \cong \overline{OC}$ (Definition of radius of a regular polygon)
(4) $\overline{OP} \cong \overline{OP}$ (Reflexive)
(5) $\triangle BPO \cong \triangle CPO$ (H.L.)
(6) $\angle BOP \cong \angle COP$ (C.P.C.T.C.)
(7) $\overline{OP}$ bisects $\angle BOC$. (Definition of angle bisector)

Practice 99
a. $36 - 9\pi$
b. 944
c. 41.52 m^3
d. $x = 12$
e. **(1)** Quadrilateral $FGHJ$ is inscribed in $\odot O$. (Given)
(2) $m\angle F = \dfrac{1}{2}m\widehat{GHJ}$ & $m\angle H = \dfrac{1}{2}m\widehat{JFG}$ (An inscribed angle is equal in measure to one-half the measure of its intercepted arc.)
(3) $m\angle F + m\angle H = \dfrac{1}{2}m\widehat{GHJ} + \dfrac{1}{2}m\widehat{JFG}$ (Addition)

(4) $m\widehat{GHJ} + m\widehat{JFG}$
$= 360$ (Arc Addition Postulate)

(5) $\frac{1}{2}m\widehat{GHJ}$

$+ \frac{1}{2}m\widehat{JFG} = 180$

(Multiplication)

(6) $m\angle F + m\angle H$
$= 180$ (Substitution)

(7) $m\angle F + m\angle G$
$+ m\angle H + m\angle J = 360$
(The sum of the measures of angles of a quadrilateral is 360.)

(8) $180 + m\angle G$
$+ m\angle J = 360$
(Substitution)

(9) $m\angle G + m\angle J$
$= 180$ (Subtraction)

Problem Set 99

1. True
2. True
3. length; width; altitude
4. base; altitude
5. altitude; sum
6. $m\widehat{AB} = 100$
7. $m\angle BDC = 55$
8. $100 + 25\sqrt{3}$ sq. in.
9. 64
10. $16 - 4\pi$
11. 100π
12. 2,592
13. 64
14. 288π
15. 5.22 m^3
16. 3
17. 11
18. 90
19. 40
20. $x = 15$

21. 2,170 apples
22. 9,090 grapes
23. **(1)** $\overleftrightarrow{AB}$ is tangent to $\odot O$ at A and $\overleftrightarrow{CD}$ is tangent to $\odot O$ at D. (Given)
    (2) $\overline{CA} \cong \overline{CD}$ (If two tangent segments are drawn to a circle from the same exterior point, then they are congruent.)
    (3) $\overleftrightarrow{AB}$ is tangent to $\odot P$ at B and $\overleftrightarrow{CD}$ is tangent to $\odot P$ at D. (Given)
    (4) $\overline{CD} \cong \overline{CB}$ (If two tangent segments are drawn to a circle from the same exterior point, then they are congruent.)
    (5) $\overline{CA} \cong \overline{CB}$ (Transitive)
    (6) $\overline{CD}$ bisects $\overline{AB}$. (Definition of bisector)
24. **(1)** Quadrilateral $ABCD$ is inscribed in $\odot O$. (Given)
    (2) $m\angle A = \frac{1}{2}m\widehat{BCD}$
    & $m\angle C = \frac{1}{2}m\widehat{DAB}$
    (An inscribed angle is equal in measure to one-half the measure of its intercepted arc.)

(3) $m\angle A + m\angle C =$
$\frac{1}{2}m\widehat{BCD} + \frac{1}{2}m\widehat{DAB}$
(Addition)
(4) $m\widehat{BCD} + m\widehat{DAB}$
$= 360$ (Arc Addition Postulate)
(5) $\frac{1}{2}m\widehat{BCD}$

$+ \frac{1}{2}m\widehat{DAB} = 180$

(Multiplication)
(6) $m\angle A + m\angle C$
$= 180$ (Substitution)
(7) $m\angle A + m\angle B$
$+ m\angle C + m\angle D = 360$
(The sum of the measures of angles of a quadrilateral is 360.)
(8) $180 + m\angle B$
$+ m\angle D = 360$
(Substitution)
(9) $m\angle B + m\angle D$
$= 180$ (Subtraction)

Practice 100

a. $16\pi + 32$
b. 448
c. 1:64
d. 5
e. **(1)** $\square EFGH$ is inscribed in $\odot O$ of radius r. (Given)
   (2) Draw diagonals EH and FG. (Two points determine a unique straight line.)
   (3) $\alpha \square EFGH =$
   $\frac{1}{2}(EH \times FG)$ (The area of a square (rhombus) is equal to one-half the product

of the lengths of the two diagonals.)

(4) $\angle GEF$ and $\angle HFE$ are right angles. (Definition of a square)

(5) $m\overset{\frown}{GHF} = 180$ and $m\overset{\frown}{EGH} = 180$ (An inscribed angle equals one-half its intercepted arc.)

(6) $\overset{\frown}{GHF}$ and $\overset{\frown}{EGH}$ are semicircles. (Definition of a semicircle)

(7) EH and FG are diameters of $\odot O$. (Definition of diameter)

(8) $EH = 2r$ and $FG = 2r$ (The length of the diameter of a circle is twice the length of the radius.)

(9) $\alpha \square EFGH = \frac{1}{2}(2r \times 2r)$ (Substitution)

(10) $\alpha \square EFGH = 2r^2$ (Multiplication)

Problem Set 100

1. False
2. False
3. similar; square
4. similar; cube
5. cylinder
6. $16 - 4\pi$
7. $25\pi + 50$
8. 112
9. 360
10. $1,200\pi$
11. 1,344 cu. in.

12. 144π
13. $125:1$
14. $4:9$
15. $27:1$
16. $4 + 2\pi$
17. $4 + 2\sqrt{2}$
18. $44°$
19. $22°$
20. 8
21. 17
22. 8
23. **(1)** From point M, draw the altitude intersecting $\overline{PQ}$ at point I. (Two points determine a unique straight line.)

    (2) $\alpha \triangle PNM = \frac{1}{2}(PN)(MI)$ and $\alpha \triangle QNM = \frac{1}{2}(QN)(MI)$ (The area of a triangle is equal to one-half the product of the base and the altitude.)

    (3) N is the midpoint of $\overline{PQ}$ (Given)

    (4) $QN = PN$ (Definition of a midpoint)

    (5) $\alpha \triangle PNM = \frac{1}{2}(QN)(MI)$ (Substitution)

    (6) $\alpha \triangle PNM = \alpha \triangle QNM$ (Substitution or transitive)

24. **(1)** $\square MNPQ$ is inscribed in $\odot O$ of radius r. (Given)

    (2) Draw diagonals MQ and NP of

$\square MNPQ$. (Two points determine a unique straight line.)

(3) $\alpha \square MNPQ = \frac{1}{2}(MQ \times NP)$ (The area of a square (rhombus) is equal to one-half the product of the lengths of the two diagonals.)

(4) $\angle PMN$ and $\angle QNM$ are right angles. (Definition of a square)

(5) $m\overset{\frown}{PQN} = 180$ and $m\overset{\frown}{MPQ} = 180$ (An inscribed angle equals one-half its intercepted arc.)

(6) $\overset{\frown}{PQN}$ and $\overset{\frown}{MPQ}$ are semicircles. (Definition of semicircle)

(7) MQ and NP are diameters of $\odot O$. (Definition of diameter)

(8) $MQ = 2r$ and $NP = 2r$ (The length of the diameter of a circle is twice the length of the radius.)

(9) $\alpha \square MNPQ = \frac{1}{2}(2r \times 2r)$ (Substitution)

(10) $\alpha \square MNPQ = 2r^2$ (Multiplication)

CHAPTER 15

Practice 101

a. $J(0,3)$, $L(4,0)$

b. $b^2 - 2c^2$

c. $27:125$

d. 8

e. **(1)** $\triangle PST \cong \triangle QRT$ and $\triangle PQT \cong \triangle SRT$ (Given)
(2) $\overline{PS} \cong \overline{QR}$ and $\overline{PQ} \cong \overline{SR}$ (C.P.C.T.C.)
(3) $PQRS$ is a parallelogram (If both pairs of opposite sides are congruent, then a quadrilateral is a parallelogram.)
(4) $\overline{PS} \parallel \overline{QR}$ and $\overline{PQ} \parallel \overline{SR}$ (Definition of a parallelogram)

Problem Set 101

1. True
2. True
3. x-coordinate; y-coordinate
4. coordinate geometry
5. cone
6. $A(0,4)$, $C(5,0)$
7. $B(-3,2)$, $D(2,-1)$
8. $Q(6,3)$
9. $102°$
10. $53°$
11. 12π
12. $y^2 - 2z^2$
13. $4:9$
14. $125:343$
15. 768
16. 220
17. $2\pi r^3$
18. $r = 2$
19. $r = 1$
20. $r = 10$
21. 11.79 feet
22. 30.94 in.
23. **(1)** $\overline{MN}$ is a diameter of $\odot O$ (Given)
(2) Angles P and Q are right angles (An inscribed angle that intercepts a semicircle is a right angle.)
(3) $\overline{MN} \cong \overline{MN}$ (Reflexive)
(4) $\overparen{MP} \cong \overparen{NQ}$ (Given)
(5) $\overline{MP} \cong \overline{NQ}$ (If two minor arcs of the same circle are congruent, then their intersecting chords are congruent.)
(6) $\triangle MNP \cong \triangle NMQ$ (Hypotenuse-Leg)
24. **(1)** $\triangle ADE \cong \triangle BCE$ and $\triangle ABE \cong \triangle DCE$ (Given)
(2) $\overline{AD} \cong \overline{BC}$ and $\overline{AB} \cong \overline{DC}$ (C.P.C.T.C.)
(3) $ABCD$ is a parallelogram (If both pairs of opposite sides are congruent, then a quadrilateral is a parallelogram.)
(4) $\overline{AD} \parallel \overline{BC}$ and $\overline{AB} \parallel \overline{DC}$ (Definition of a parallelogram)

Practice 102

a. $F(a,0)$, $I(b,0)$

b. $(-1.5, 3.5)$

c. $EH = 6$, $HG = 2\sqrt{2}$

d. 7

e. **(1)** $\overline{DF} \parallel \overline{VG}$ (Given)
(2) Draw chord DG (Two points determine a unique straight line.)
(3) $m\angle FDG = m\angle DGV$ (If two parallel lines are cut by a transversal, then their alternate interior angles are equal.)
(4) $\frac{1}{2}m\angle FDG = \frac{1}{2}m\angle DGV$ (Multiplication)
(5) $m\overparen{FG} = \frac{1}{2}m\angle FDG$ and $m\overparen{DV} = \frac{1}{2}m\angle DGV$ (An inscribed angle is equal in measure to one-half the measure of its intercepted arc.)
(6) $m\overparen{FG} = m\overparen{DV}$ (Substitution or Transitive)
(7) $m\overparen{FG} + m\overparen{VG} = m\overparen{DV} + m\overparen{VG}$ (Addition)
(8) $m\overparen{FGV} = m\overparen{FG} + m\overparen{VG}$ and $m\overparen{DVG} = m\overparen{DV} + m\overparen{VG}$

(Arc Addition Postulate)

(9) $m\overarc{FGV} = m\overarc{DVG}$ (Substitution)

(10) $\angle KDF \cong \angle KFD$ (Inscribed angles that intercept congruent arcs are congruent)

(11) $\overline{FK} \cong \overline{DK}$ (Converse of Base Angles Theorem)

Problem Set 102

1. True
2. True
3. base; altitude
4. π; radius
5. area of a base; altitude
6. $V(a,a), W(a,0)$
7. $M(0,c)$, $P(a,0)$
8. $(-1,3)$
9. $(\frac{1}{2},-4)$
10. $AC = 5$
11. $JK = 6$, $KL = 5$
12. $RS = 5$, $ST = \sqrt{10}$
13. 7.5
14. $144\pi - 72$
15. $36 + 12\sqrt{2}$
16. 30
17. 358 sq. in.
18. $36 + 9\sqrt{3}$
19. 392 cm^2
20. $x = 6$
21. 240
22. $h = 20$
23. **(1)** $\overline{HM} \parallel \overline{IN}$, $\overline{HM} \parallel \overline{GJ}$, $\overline{GJ} \parallel \overline{IN}$,

$\overline{HI} \parallel \overline{MN}$, $\overline{HG} \parallel \overline{MJ}$, $\overline{GI} \parallel \overline{JN}$ (Given)

(2). $HGJM$, $GINJ$ and $HINM$ are parallelograms (Definition of parallelogram)

(3). $\overline{HG} \cong \overline{MJ}$, $\overline{GI} \cong \overline{JN}$, $\overline{HI} \cong \overline{MN}$ (If a quadrilateral is a parallelogram, then both pairs of opposite sides are congruent.)

(4). $\triangle HGI \cong \triangle MJN$ (S. S. S.)

24. **(1)** $\overline{TR} \parallel \overline{US}$ (Given)

(2) Draw chord TS (Two points determine a unique straight line.)

(3) $m\angle RTS = m\angle TSU$ (If two parallel lines are cut by a transversal, then their alternate interior angles are equal.)

(4) $\frac{1}{2}m\angle RTS = \frac{1}{2}m\angle TSU$ (Multiplication)

(5) $m\overarc{RS} = \frac{1}{2}m\angle RTS$ & $m\overarc{TU} = \frac{1}{2}m\angle TSU$ (An inscribed angle is equal in measure to one-half the measure of its intercepted arc)

(6) $m\overarc{RS} = m\overarc{TU}$ (Substitution or Transitive)

(7) $m\overarc{RS} + m\overarc{US} = m\overarc{TU} + m\overarc{US}$ (Addition)

(8) $m\overarc{RSU} = m\overarc{RS} + m\overarc{US}$ and $m\overarc{TUS} = m\overarc{TU} + m\overarc{US}$ (Arc Addition Postulate)

(9) $m\overarc{RSU} = m\overarc{TUS}$ (Substitution)

(10) $\angle VTR \cong \angle VRT$ (Inscribed angles that intercept congruent arcs are congruent)

(11) $\overline{RV} \cong \overline{TV}$ (Converse of Base Angles Theorem)

Practice 103

a. $(-\frac{1}{2},-\frac{5}{2})$
b. $c-b$
c. Perpendicular
d. 7.84
e. **(1)** $\overline{ZF} \cong \overline{ZG}$ (Given)

(2) $\angle ZFG \cong \angle ZGF$ (Base Angles Theorem)

(3) $m\angle ZGF = \frac{1}{2}m\overarc{HEF}$ and $m\angle ZFG = \frac{1}{2}m\overarc{EHG}$ (An inscribed angle is equal in measure to one-half the measure of its intercepted arc.)

(4) $\frac{1}{2}m\overset{\frown}{HEF} =$

$\frac{1}{2}m\overset{\frown}{EHG}$ (Transitive or substitution)

(5) $m\overset{\frown}{HEF} = m\overset{\frown}{EHG}$ (Multiplication)

(6) $m\overset{\frown}{HE} + m\overset{\frown}{EF} = m\overset{\frown}{HEF}$ and $m\overset{\frown}{EH} + m\overset{\frown}{HG} = m\overset{\frown}{EHG}$ (Arc Addition)

(7) $m\overset{\frown}{HE} + m\overset{\frown}{EF} = m\overset{\frown}{EH} + m\overset{\frown}{HG}$ (Substitution)

(8) $m\overset{\frown}{EF} = m\overset{\frown}{HG}$ (Subtraction)

(9) $\overline{EF} \cong \overline{HG}$ (If two minor arcs of the same circle are congruent, then their intersecting chords are congruent.)

(10) $\overline{EY} \perp \overline{FG}$ at point Y and $\overline{HX} \perp \overline{FG}$ at point X (Given)

(11) $m\angle EYF$ and $m\angle HXG$ are right angles. (Perpendicular lines intersect to form 4 right angles.)

(12) $\angle EYF \cong \angle HXG$ (All right angles are congruent.)

(13) $\Delta EFY \cong \Delta HGX$ (A.A.S.)

(14) $\overline{EY} \cong \overline{HX}$ (C.P.C.T.C.)

Problem Set 103

1. False
2. False
3. negative reciprocals
4. triangle
5. rhombus
6. C, B, A
7. C has a negative slope, A has a positive slope
8. $(\frac{-a+c}{2}, \frac{b+d}{2})$
9. $(-\frac{1}{2}, -3)$
10. $4\sqrt{2}$
11. $a-d$
12. 2
13. -3
14. Parallel
15. Neither
16. 42π
17. $3.125\pi - 6$
18. 816 cu. in.
19. 200
20. 36
21. 2
22. 5.23
23. **(1)** $\overline{LN}$ and $\overline{RN}$ are secant segments. $\overleftrightarrow{NT}$ is tangent to both $\odot O$ and $\odot P$ at point T (Given)
    (2) $LN \times MN = (NT)^2$ and $RN \times QN = (NT)^2$ (If a tangent segment and a secant segment are drawn to a circle from the same exterior point, then the square of the length of the tangent segment is equal to

the product of the lengths of the secant segment and its external segment.)
    (3) $LN \times MN = RN \times QN$ (Transitive)

24. **(1)** $\overline{MQ} \cong \overline{MS}$ (Given)
    (2) $\angle MSQ \cong \angle MQS$ (Base Angles Thm.)
    (3) $m\angle MSQ = \frac{1}{2}m\overset{\frown}{QPR}$ and $m\angle MQS = \frac{1}{2}m\overset{\frown}{PRS}$ (An inscribed angle is equal in measure to one-half the measure of its intercepted arc.)
    (4) $\frac{1}{2}m\overset{\frown}{QPR} = \frac{1}{2}m\overset{\frown}{PRS}$ (Transitive or substitution)
    (5) $m\overset{\frown}{QPR} = m\overset{\frown}{PRS}$ (Multiplication)
    (6) $m\overset{\frown}{QP} + m\overset{\frown}{PR} = m\overset{\frown}{QPR}$ and $m\overset{\frown}{PR} + m\overset{\frown}{RS} = m\overset{\frown}{PRS}$ (Arc Addition)
    (7) $m\overset{\frown}{QP} + m\overset{\frown}{PR} = m\overset{\frown}{PR} + m\overset{\frown}{RS}$ (Substitution)
    (8) $m\overset{\frown}{QP} = m\overset{\frown}{RS}$ (Subtraction)
    (9) $\overline{QP} \cong \overline{RS}$ (If two minor arcs of the same circle are

congruent, then their intersecting chords are congruent.)

(10) $\overline{PI} \perp \overline{QS}$ at point I and $\overline{RJ} \perp \overline{QS}$ at point J (Given)

(11) $m\angle PIQ$ and $m\angle RJS$ are right angles. (Perpendicular lines intersect to form 4 right angles.)

(12) $\angle PIQ \cong \angle RJS$ (All right angles are congruent.)

(13) $\triangle PIQ \cong \triangle RJS$ (A.A.S.)

(14) $\overline{PI} \cong \overline{RJ}$ (C.P.C.T.C.)

Practice 104

a. 12

b. $\sqrt{a^2 + b^2}$

c. $y + 2 = 1(x + 4)$

d. $(4,5)$

e. **(1)** $m\angle JIM = \frac{1}{2}m\widehat{JN}$

(An inscribed angle is equal in measure to one-half the measure of its intercepted arc.)

(2) $m\angle KJN = \frac{1}{2}m\widehat{JN}$ (The measure of an angle formed by a tangent and a chord drawn to the point of tangency is equal to one-half the measure of the intercepted arc.)

(3) $\angle KJN \cong \angle JIM$ (Transitive)

(4) $\overline{KJ}$ is tangent to $\odot O$ at point J (Given)

(5) $m\angle IJM$ is a right angle. (If a radius is drawn to the point of tangency of a tangent line, then the radius is perpendicular to the tangent line.)

(6) $\overline{IJ} \parallel \overline{LK}$ (Given)

(7) $m\angle LKJ$ is a right angle. (If two parallel lines are cut (crossed) by a transversal, then interior angles on the same side of the transversal are supplementary.)

(8) $\angle LKJ \cong \angle IJM$ (All right angles are congruent.)

(9) $\triangle JKL \sim \triangle IJM$ (A.A. Similarity)

(10) $\frac{JL}{IM} = \frac{KL}{JM}$ (Converse of Definition of Similar Triangles)

Problem Set 104

1. True
2. True
3. $V = \pi r^2 a$
4. length; width; altitude
5. $V = \frac{4}{3}\pi r^3$
6. $A(0,b)$, $B(a,b)$
7. $G(a,a)$, $H(a,0)$
8. 48
9. 196π
10. 16
11. $AB = 5$, $BC = 5$
12. $\sqrt{a^2 + b^2}$
13. $44°$
14. $22°$
15. 0
16. $\frac{1}{2}$
17. $y = -x + 3$
18. $y = 4x - 2$
19. $y + 3 = 2(x + 5)$
20. $2\sqrt{2}$
21. 4
22. $(5,5)$
23. **(1)** Draw $\overline{KL}$, the perpendicular segment from K to $\overline{GH}$. (Through a point not on a line, there exists exactly one perpendicular to the given line.)

(2) $\overrightarrow{GH} \parallel \overrightarrow{JK}$ (Given)

(3) The distance from K to $\overline{GH}$ is KL. (Definition of distance between a point and a line.)

(4) The distance from J to $\overline{GH}$ is KL. (The distance between parallel lines is constant.)

(5) $\overline{KL}$ is the altitude of both $\triangle GKH$ and $\triangle GJH$ (Definition of altitude)

(6) $\alpha\triangle GKH = \frac{1}{2}GH \times KL$ and

$\alpha \triangle GJH = \frac{1}{2} GH \times KL$

(Area of a triangle)

(7) $\alpha \triangle GJH = \alpha \triangle GKH$ (Transitive)

24. (1) $m\angle QPU = \frac{1}{2} m\overgroup{QV}$ (An inscribed angle is equal in measure to one-half the measure of its intercepted arc.)

(2) $m\angle RQV = \frac{1}{2} m\overgroup{QV}$ (The measure of an angle formed by a tangent and a chord drawn to the point of tangency is equal to one-half the measure of the intercepted arc.)

(3) $\angle RQV \cong \angle QPU$ (Transitive)

(4) $\overline{RQ}$ is tangent to $\odot O$ at point Q (Given)

(5) $m\angle PQU$ is a right angle. (If a radius is drawn to the point of tangency of a tangent line, then the radius is perpendicular to the tangent line.)

(6) $\overline{PQ} \parallel \overline{SR}$ (Given)

(7) $m\angle SRQ$ is a right angle. (If two parallel lines are cut (crossed) by a transversal, then interior angles on the same side of the

transversal are supplementary.)

(8) $\angle SRQ \cong \angle PQU$ (All right angles are congruent.)

(9) $\triangle QRS \sim \triangle PQU$ (A.A. Similarity)

(10) $\frac{QS}{PU} = \frac{RS}{QU}$ (Converse of Definition of Similar Triangles)

Practice 105

a. $E(2c, 0)$

b. $\left(\frac{b}{2}, \frac{c}{2} \right)$

c. $\sqrt{(a-c)^2 + b^2}$

d. $y - 5 = 3(x - 2)$ or $y + 7 = 3(x + 2)$

e. By the midpoint formula, the coordinates of point J are $\left(\frac{0+a}{2}, \frac{0+b}{2} \right)$ or $\left(\frac{a}{2}, \frac{b}{2} \right)$. Then by the distance formula,

$JI = \sqrt{\left(\frac{a}{2} - a \right)^2 + \left(\frac{b}{2} - 0 \right)^2}$

$= \sqrt{\left(-\frac{a}{2} \right)^2 + \left(\frac{b}{2} \right)^2}$

$= \sqrt{\frac{a^2 + b^2}{4}}$

$= \frac{\sqrt{a^2 + b^2}}{2}$.

Similarly, by the

distance formula, $JH =$

$\sqrt{\left(a - \frac{a}{2} \right)^2 + \left(b - \frac{b}{2} \right)^2}$

$= \sqrt{\left(\frac{a}{2} \right)^2 + \left(\frac{b}{2} \right)^2}$

$= \sqrt{\frac{a^2 + b^2}{4}}$

$= \frac{\sqrt{a^2 + b^2}}{2}$. Then,

by substitution or transitive, $JI = JH$.

Problem Set 105

1. True
2. False
3. $C = 2\pi r$
4. altitude; one-half
5. sphere
6. $S(0, a)$, $T(b, a)$, $V(c, 0)$
7. $J(2a, 0)$
8. C, A, B
9. C has a negative slope, A and B have positive slopes
10. $\left(\frac{a}{2}, b \right)$
11. $\left(\frac{a}{2}, \frac{b}{2} \right)$
12. $OP = 3$
13. $\sqrt{(b-a)^2 + c^2}$
14. 176
15. 16 cu. in.
16. $-\frac{2}{3}$
17. $\frac{5}{3}$

18. $y+5=\dfrac{2}{3}(x+3)$

19. $y-3=\dfrac{7}{3}(x-2)$ or

$y+4=\dfrac{7}{3}(x+1)$

20. 36

21. $s=6$

22. $\sqrt{(x-h)^2+(y-k)^2}$

23. By the distance formula, $FH=$

$\sqrt{(a-0)^2+(b-0)^2}$

$=\sqrt{a^2+b^2}$ and

$GJ=$

$\sqrt{(0-a)^2+(b-0)^2}$

$=\sqrt{(-a)^2+(b)^2}$

$=\sqrt{a^2+b^2}$. Then, by substitution or the transitive property, $FH=GJ$.

24. By the midpoint formula, the coordinates of point D are

$\left(\dfrac{0+a}{2},\dfrac{b+0}{2}\right)$ or

$\left(\dfrac{a}{2},\dfrac{b}{2}\right)$. Then by the distance formula,

$AD=$

$\sqrt{\left(\dfrac{a}{2}-0\right)^2+\left(\dfrac{b}{2}-0\right)^2}$

$=\sqrt{\left(\dfrac{a}{2}\right)^2+\left(\dfrac{b}{2}\right)^2}$

$=\sqrt{\dfrac{a^2+b^2}{4}}$

$=\dfrac{\sqrt{a^2+b^2}}{2}$.

Similarly, by the distance formula,

$BD=$

$\sqrt{\left(\dfrac{a}{2}-0\right)^2+\left(\dfrac{b}{2}-b\right)^2}$

$=\sqrt{\left(\dfrac{a}{2}\right)^2+\left(-\dfrac{b}{2}\right)^2}$

$=\sqrt{\dfrac{a^2+b^2}{4}}$

$=\dfrac{\sqrt{a^2+b^2}}{2}$. Then,

by substitution or transitive, $AD=BD$.

Practice 106

a. 5

b. 160 cm³

c. $y-2=-\dfrac{1}{2}(x-2)$

d. 32

e. Any intersection points are solutions to the system:

$\begin{cases} y=x+2 \\ (x-3)^2+(y-3)^2=4 \end{cases}$

Substituting $x+2$ in for y:

$(x-3)^2+(x+2-3)^2$

$=4$;

$(x-3)^2+(x-1)^2=4$

$x^2-6x+9+x^2$

$\qquad\qquad -2x+1=4$

$2x^2-8x+10=4$

$x^2-4x+3=0$

$(x-3)(x-1)=0$

$x=3$ or $x=1$, so the solutions are (3, 5) and (1, 3). Since the system has two solu-

tions, the line intersects the circle in two points and is therefore a secant line.

Problem Set 106

1. False

2. True

3. $y=mx+b$

4. $V=\dfrac{4}{3}\pi r^3$

5. sector

6. $OP=\sqrt{13}$, $PQ=3$

7. $OA=5$

8. 10

9. 10

10. 740

11. $1,280$ cm³

12. 405π

13. $\dfrac{3}{4}$

14. 8

15. $-\dfrac{5}{2}$

16. $\dfrac{7}{6}$

17. $y+3=\dfrac{3}{2}(x+2)$

18. $y+1=-1(x-2)$ or $y-5=-1(x+4)$

19. $y-1=\dfrac{1}{2}(x-4)$

20. $\sqrt{170}$

21. 72

22. 16

23. $AD=a$ and $BC=a+b-b=a$, so $AD=BC$ by substitution. By the distance formula, $AB=$

$$\sqrt{(b-0)^2+(c-0)^2}$$
$$=\sqrt{b^2+c^2} \text{ and}$$
$$DC =$$
$$\sqrt{(a+b-a)^2+(c-0)^2}$$
$$=\sqrt{b^2+c^2}, \text{ so by}$$
substitution
$$AB = DC.$$

24. Any intersection points are solutions to the system:

$$\begin{cases} y = x+1 \\ (x-3)^2+(y-2)^2 = 4 \end{cases}$$

Substituting $x+1$ in for y:

$$(x-3)^2+(x+1-2)^2 = 4$$
$$(x-3)^2+(x-1)^2 = 4$$
$$x^2-6x+9+x^2$$
$$-2x+1 = 4$$
$$2x^2-8x+10 = 4$$
$$x^2-4x+3 = 0$$
$$(x-3)(x-1) = 0$$

$x = 3$ or $x = 1$, so the solutions are (3, 4) and (1, 2). Since the system has two solutions, the line intersects the circle in two points and is therefore a secant line.

ADDITIONAL TOPICS

Practice 107

a. $\angle G$ should have the same measure as $\angle F$

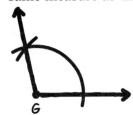

b. $8\pi - 16$

c. $64:125$

d. $y = 60$

e. By the midpoint formula, the coordinates of S are $\left(\dfrac{a}{2}, \dfrac{b}{2}\right)$ and the coordinates of T are $\left(\dfrac{a+d}{2}, \dfrac{b}{2}\right)$. The slope of $\overline{ST}$ is

$$\dfrac{\dfrac{b}{2} - \dfrac{b}{2}}{\dfrac{a+d}{2} - \dfrac{a}{2}} = 0.$$ The slope of $\overline{PR}$ is $\dfrac{0-0}{d-0} = 0$. Since their slopes are equal, $\overline{ST} \parallel \overline{PR}$. Since $\overline{PR}$ and $\overline{ST}$ are horizontal, the length of each is the difference in x-coordinates. So, $PR = d - 0 = d$ and $ST = \dfrac{a+d}{2} - \dfrac{a}{2} = \dfrac{d}{2}$.

Thus, $ST = \dfrac{1}{2}PR$.

Problem Set 107

1. True
2. True
3. $x^2 + y^2 = r^2$
4. base; altitude
5. slant height
6. $B(a,d)$, $D(c,b)$
7. $L(0,b)$, $J(b,b)$
8. $\left(\dfrac{c-a}{2}, \dfrac{b+d}{2}\right)$
9. $(-2,-2)$
10. $\overline{PQ}$ should be the same length as $\overline{LM}$

11. $\angle C$ should have the same measure as $\angle B$

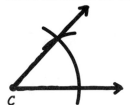

12. $\angle E$ should have the same measure as $\angle D$

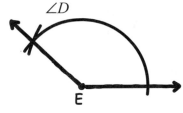

13. 356 cm^2
14. $27:343$
15. 18
16. $2\pi - 4$
17. $y + 3 = \dfrac{1}{3}(x+4)$
18. $y = -5x - 4$
19. 127
20. $y = 54$
21. S.A.S. Congruence
22. S.A.S. Similarity or A.A. Similarity
23. Draw diagonals FH and GJ. By the distance formula, $FH = $
$$\sqrt{(c-0)^2 + (b-0)^2} = $$
$$\sqrt{c^2 + b^2} \text{ and } GJ = .$$
$$\sqrt{(a+c-a)^2 + (0-b)^2}$$
$$= \sqrt{c^2 + b^2} \text{ By substitution, } FH = GJ,$$
so the diagonals are congruent.

24. By the midpoint formula, the coordinates of D are $\left(\dfrac{a}{2}, \dfrac{b}{2}\right)$ and the coordinates of E are $\left(\dfrac{a+c}{2}, \dfrac{b}{2}\right)$. The slope of $\overline{DE}$ is
$$\dfrac{\dfrac{b}{2} - \dfrac{b}{2}}{\dfrac{a+c}{2} - \dfrac{a}{2}} = 0.$$ The slope of $\overline{AC}$ is
$$\dfrac{0-0}{c-0} = 0.$$ Since their slopes are equal, $\overline{DE} \parallel \overline{AC}$. Since $\overline{AC}$ and $\overline{DE}$ are horizontal, the length of each is the difference in x-coordinates. So, $AC = c - 0 = c$ and $DE = \dfrac{a+c}{2} - \dfrac{a}{2} = \dfrac{c}{2}$.

Thus, $DE = \dfrac{1}{2}AC$.

Practice 108

a. $3\pi + 2$ cm^2

b. The middle ray should bisect $\angle K$

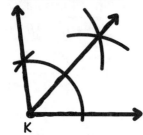

c. $T(a, a\sqrt{3})$

d. $D(0, 2b-c)$

e. By the midpoint formula, I has coordinates (b,c) and J has coordinates $(d+a,c)$. Subtracting x-coordinates, the horizontal distances are $IJ = d+a-b$, $EH = 2a$, and $FG = 2d-2b$. So
$$\frac{1}{2}(EH+FG) =$$
$$\frac{1}{2}(2a+2d-2b)$$
$$= a+d-b$$
$$= d+a-b = IJ.$$

Problem Set 108

1. True
2. False
3. base; vertex
4. π; radius
5. $(x-h)^2 + (y-k)^2$ $= r^2$
6. 17
7. $OL = \sqrt{b^2+c^2}$, $MN = \sqrt{b^2+c^2}$
8. πa^2
9. $48\pi + 32$ sq. in.

10. The vertical segment should bisect $\overline{FG}$.

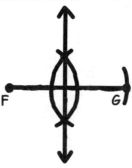

11. The middle ray should bisect $\angle H$

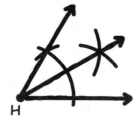

12. The middle ray should bisect $\angle J$

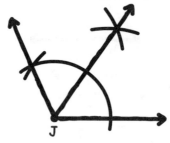

13. $156 + 60\sqrt{2}$
14. 96π m^2
15. A, B, C
16. C has positive slope, A and B have negative slopes
17. $y - 11 = -\dfrac{7}{2}(x-1)$ or $y + 3 = -\dfrac{7}{2}(x-5)$
18. $y - 7 = \dfrac{1}{2}(x-8)$
19. $A(-a, 0)$, $B(0, a\sqrt{3})$
20. $N(2a-c, 0)$

21. 960 cm^2
22. 960 in.^{2}
23. Draw the diagonals $\overline{PR}$ and $\overline{OQ}$. The slope of $\overline{PR}$ is $\dfrac{4-0}{3-5} = \dfrac{4}{-2} = -2$. The slope of $\overline{OQ}$ is $\dfrac{4-0}{8-0} = \dfrac{4}{8} = \dfrac{1}{2}$. Since the slopes -2 and $\dfrac{1}{2}$ are negative reciprocals, $\overline{PR} \perp \overline{OQ}$.

24. By the midpoint formula, E has coordinates (a,b) and F has coordinates $(c+d,b)$. Subtracting x-coordinates, the horizontal distances are $EF = c+d-a$, $AD = 2d$, and $BC = 2c-2a$. So
$$\frac{1}{2}(AD+BC) =$$
$$\frac{1}{2}(2d+2c-2a)$$
$$= d+c-a$$
$$= c+d-a = EF.$$

Practice 109

a. $2\sqrt{3} + \dfrac{4}{3}\pi$

b. $4\sqrt{2}$

c. $y + 3 = \dfrac{1}{2}(x-1)$

d. $6\sqrt{3}$ cm

e. **(1)** $\overline{PQ}$ is a diameter of $\odot O$ (Given)
(2) $\angle PSQ$ is a right angle (An inscribed angle that intercepts a semicircle is a right angle.)
(3) $m\angle PSQ = 90$ (Definition of a right angle)
(4) $m\angle PRQ > m\angle PSQ$ (The measure of an exterior angle of a triangle is greater than the measure of either of the remote interior angles.)
(5) $m\angle PRQ > 90$ (Substitution)
(6) $\angle PRQ$ is obtuse. (Definition of an obtuse angle)
(7) $\triangle PRQ$ is obtuse (Definition of an obtuse triangle)

Problem Set 109
1. True
2. True
3. translation
4. reflection
5. transformation
6. $-\dfrac{1}{2}$
7. $\dfrac{b}{a}$
8. $32\pi - 32$
9. $8\sqrt{3} + \dfrac{16}{3}\pi$
10. Reflection
11. Rotation
12. 13

13. The vertical segment should bisect $\overline{KL}$.

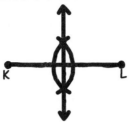

14. The middle ray should bisect $\angle P$

15. $28°, 96°, 56°$
16. $23°, 134°, 23°$
17. $y + 4 = \dfrac{2}{3}(x - 6)$
18. $y + 1 = 1(x + 2)$
19. 3 cm
20. $3\sqrt{3}$ cm
21. 42
22. The 18-inch pizza
23. **(1)** $\overset{\frown}{JK} \cong \overset{\frown}{KL}$ (Given)
(2) $\angle JMK \cong \angle KJL$ (Inscribed angles that intercept congruent arcs are congruent.)
(3) $\angle JKN \cong \angle JKN$ (Reflexive)
(4) $\triangle JKN \sim \triangle MKJ$ (A.A. Similarity)
24. **(1)** $\overline{AC}$ is a diameter of $\odot O$ (Given)
(2) $\angle ADC$ is a right angle. (An inscribed angle that intercepts a semicircle is a right angle.)
(3) $m\angle ADC = 90$ (Definition of a right angle)

(4) $m\angle ABC > m\angle ADC$ (The measure of an exterior angle of a triangle is greater than the measure of either of the remote interior angles.)
(5) $m\angle ABC > 90$ (Substitution)
(6) $\angle ABC$ is obtuse. (Definition of an obtuse angle)
(7) $\triangle ABC$ is obtuse (Definition of an obtuse triangle)

Practice 110
a. 2π
b. Each side should be bisected.

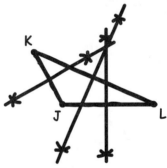

c. $9\sqrt{3}$ in.
d. 8
e. **(1)** $\overline{CO}$ is a diameter of $\odot P$; $\overline{AC}$ is a chord of $\odot O$ (Given)
(2) $\angle CBO$ is a right angle (An inscribed angle that intercepts a semicircle is a right angle.)
(3) $\overline{OB} \perp \overline{AC}$ (Definition of perpendicular)

(4) $AB = BC$ (If a line through the center of a circle is perpendicular to a chord, it also bisects the chord.)

Problem Set 110

1. True
2. True
3. rotation
4. Albert Einstein
5. negative reciprocals
6. $AC = \sqrt{4a^2 + b^2}$, $BD = \sqrt{4a^2 + b^2}$
7. $PQ = 2a$
8. $72 - 18\pi$
9. $\dfrac{\pi}{2}$
10. Rotation
11. Reflection
12. $2\sqrt{10}$
13. Each angle should be bisected.

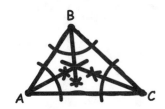

14. Each side should be bisected.

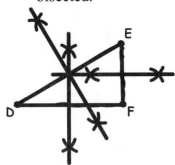

15. 1,680 cubic inches
16. 32π ft^3

17. $y + 2 = \dfrac{3}{2}(x + 3)$
18. $y = \dfrac{2}{3}x + 7$
19. $6\sqrt{3}$ in.
20. 9 in.
21. 50
22. 80π
23. **(1)** Chords $\overline{CF}$ and $\overline{DG}$ intersect at point E (Given)
    (2) $\angle G \cong \angle F$ and $\angle C \cong \angle D$ (Inscribed angles that intercept the same arc are congruent.)
    (3) $\triangle GCE \sim \triangle FDE$ (A.A. Similarity)
    (4) $\dfrac{CG}{DF} = \dfrac{GE}{FE}$ (Converse of definition of similar triangles.)
24. **(1)** $\overline{QP}$ is a diameter of $\odot O$; $\overline{QS}$ is a chord of $\odot P$ (Given)
    (2) $\angle QRP$ is a right angle (An inscribed angle that intercepts a semicircle is a right angle.)
    (3) $\overline{PR} \perp \overline{QS}$ (Definition of perpendicular)
    (4) $QR = RS$ (If a line through the center of a circle is perpendicular to a chord, it also bisects the chord.)

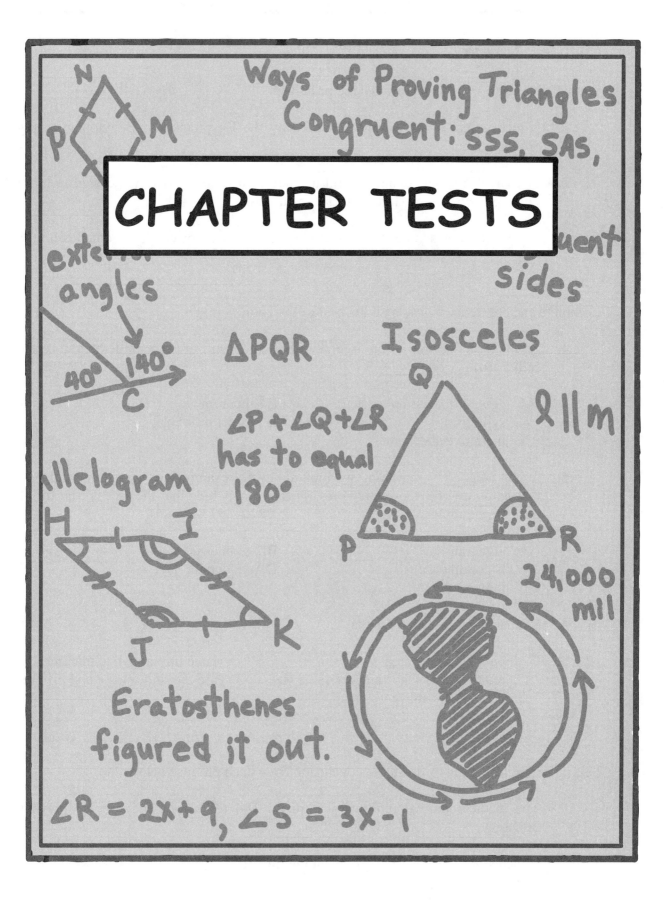

N

P

M

Ways of Proving Triangles
Congruent: SSS, SAS,

CHAPTER TESTS

uent
sides

exterior
angles

40°   140°
       C

ΔPQR

∠P + ∠Q + ∠R
has to equal
180°

Isosceles

Q

ℓ ∥ m

P   R

24,000
mil

allelogram

H   I

J   K

Eratosthenes
figured it out.

∠R = 2x + 9, ∠S = 3x - 1

Chapter 1 Test

Tell whether each sentence below is True or False.

1. Inductive reasoning, the method used by the Egyptians and Babylonians, only gives probable facts.

2. The Greek mathematician Euclid decided to use only inductive reasoning in his book *The Elements*, which starts with 10 postulates.

3. In deductive reasoning, as long as you've reasoned correctly, the conclusion *has* to be true.

Complete each sentence below with the best of the choices given.

4. The final conclusion of an argument that has been proven with deductive reasoning is called a(n) _____.

   A. geometrical complexity   B. theorem
   C. syllogism   D. direct proof
   E. inductive statement

5. In _____ reasoning we look at several examples of something and find a fact that holds true for those examples. Then we conclude that the fact is true for all other possible examples.

   A. algebraic   B. geometric
   C. trigonometric D. deductive
   E. inductive

6. Similar figures are figures that _____.

   A. have the same area   B. have the same line thickness
   C. are the same shape and the same size D. are the same shape and different size
   E. none of the above

Use inductive reasoning to finish the conclusion from each premise below.

7. The medical journal reported that in all 184 test cases, the vaccine prevented the infection.

   Conclusion: _____ prevent the infection.

8. In circle O, the distance from the center O to point P equals 2 inches, the distance from the center O to point Q equals 2 inches, and the distance from the center O to point R equals 2 inches.

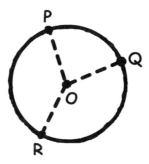

Conclusion: The distance from the center O to any point on the circle is _____.

Identify the premise and the conclusion of the conditional statement below.

9. If a team has only an inch to go on fourth down, then they absolutely must go for it.

Rewrite the sentence below in conditional ("if-then") form.

10. All runaway grocery carts hate it when the parking lot slopes upward.

Draw a Venn diagram to represent each set of conditional statements below.

11. If a being is a Venusian, then it is six-legged. If QZ3 is a Venusian, then QZ3 is six-legged.

12. All male pink flamingos wish they were blue. Pauley is a male pink flamingo. So Pauley wishes he were blue.

Write conditional statements to represent each Venn diagram below.

13.

14.

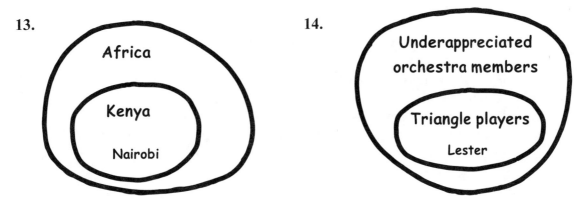

Tell whether each argument below is an example of inductive or deductive reasoning.

15. If all the people at Maria's party are 15 years old, and if Sandra is at Maria's party, then Sandra must be 15 years old.

16. If the first 3 bull-riding contestants wore cowboy hats, then all of the bull-riding contestants will wear cowboy hats.

Tell whether the arguments below are valid or invalid deductions.

17. Since all pearl divers know how to swim and Suzy knows how to swim, Suzy must be a pearl diver.

18. All teenagers have bad hair days, and Chloe is a teenager, so Chloe has bad hair days.

Use deductive reasoning to write the conclusion for each set of statements below.

19. If a man is batting in the cleanup position, then he better be a slugger. If Gary hopes to bat in the cleanup position one day,_____.

20. All elephants are afraid of mice, and Jumbo is an elephant. Therefore, _____.

Assuming inductive reasoning was used, finish the set of facts to fit each conclusion below.

21. The police officer _____ of the first five drivers who stopped at the traffic light.

Conclusion: The police officer shined his flashlight in the faces of all the drivers who stop at the traffic light.

Tell the theorem that is proved by the set of statements below.

22. If the scoop falls off the cone, the car seat will get messy.
If the car seat gets messy, the driver will become distracted.
If the driver becomes distracted, he will swerve off the road.
If the driver swerves off the road, he will hit the fire hydrant.

Complete a direct proof for each theorem by rearranging the statements in logical order.

23.   Theorem: If the bride stares for too long into the groom's eyes, Brenda won't get married next.

If the cake-cutting is delayed by half an hour, then Brenda, one of the bridesmaids, will have to leave early.
If she does not catch the bouquet, Brenda won't get married next.
If Brenda leaves early, she will not catch the bouquet.
If the bride stares for too long into the groom's eyes, she will delay the cutting of the cake by half an hour.

24.   Theorem: If Mom drops her pots and pans, all the neighbors will wake up.

If the baby begins to cry, the dog will start to bark.
If the pots and pans hit the floor, the baby will begin to cry.
If Mom drops her pots and pans, they will hit the floor.
If the dog starts to bark, all the neighbors will wake up.

Chapter 2 Test

Tell whether each sentence below is True or False.

1. In geometry every single term must be defined.

2. Collinear points are points that lie on the same line.

3. All obtuse angles are congruent.

Complete each sentence below by filling in the blanks.

4. A _____ is a set of points that forms a flat surface which extends forever in all directions and has length and width, but no depth.

5. $\overrightarrow{BD}$ is the _____ of $\angle ABC$ if D lies in the interior of $\angle ABC$ and $m\angle ABD = m\angle DBC$.

6. An angle's end point is called the _____ of the angle.

7. _____ determine a unique line.

Complete each sentence below by filling in the blanks. Also name the property it states.

8. If equals are _____ by equals, the results are _____: If $a = b$, then $ac = bc$.

9. If $a = b$, then either a or b may be _____ for the other in any equation.

Answer each question below.

10. Tell whether each symbol below could represent a point, line, plane, line segment, ray, or angle.
    a. $\overline{GH}$ b. $\angle W$ c. $\overrightarrow{ST}$

11. How many end points does a line segment have? a ray? a line?

Draw a Venn diagram to represent the set of conditional statements below.

12. To pass your driver's test, you have to stop at all red lights. Ramona passed her driver's test, so she must have stopped at all red lights.

Write conditional statements to represent the Venn diagram below.

13.

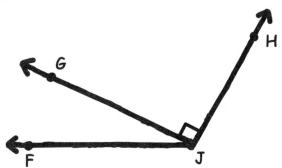

Beard goes all the way down to chest

True mountain men

Travis

Use Betweenness of Points or Rays to answer each question below.

14. If point A lies in the interior of $\angle BCD$ and if $m\angle BCA = 22$, $m\angle BCD = 105$, and $m\angle ACD = 83$, then which of the following rays is between the other two: $\overrightarrow{CA}$, $\overrightarrow{CB}$, $\overrightarrow{CD}$?

15. If K-L-M (point L is between points K and M), and if $KM = 11\frac{1}{4}$ and $KL = 3\frac{1}{2}$, then find LM.

Use the definition of a segment or angle bisector to answer each question below.

16. If $\overrightarrow{VW}$ bisects $\overline{PS}$ at point V, and if $PS = 29.2$, then find the length PV.

17. If $\overrightarrow{NQ}$ bisects $\angle MNP$, and if $m\angle QNM = 67$, then find $m\angle MNP$.

Answer each question below.

18. Name the obtuse angle below. Then measure $\angle GJF$ with a protractor and tell what kind of angle it is.

Tell whether the arguments below are valid or invalid deductions.

19. All fish have gills, and all sharks are fish. Therefore, all sharks have gills.

20. Pam wears goofy outfits. All mascots for professional sports teams wear goofy outfits, so Pam must be a mascot for a professional sports team.

Use deductive reasoning to write the conclusion for each set of statements below.

21. If a bona fide soprano can shatter glass with her voice, and if Beverly is a bona fide soprano, then _____.

Complete a direct proof for the theorem below by rearranging the statements in logical order.

22. Theorem: If the explorer's hunch is wrong, then he and the crew will end up eating shoe leather for breakfast.

If his map is off by 1,000 miles, he and his crew will run out of food before they reach the islands.
If they run out of food before they reach the islands, they will all begin to starve.
If the explorer's hunch is wrong, then his map will be off by 1,000 miles.
If they all begin to starve, he and the crew will end up eating shoe leather for breakfast.

Reverse each definition below and tell whether it passes the reversibility test.

23. Michelangelo was a famous artist.

24. A BLT is a sandwich containing only bacon, lettuce, and tomato.

Chapter 3 Test

Tell whether each sentence below is True or False.

1. Vertical angles are a pair of adjacent angles whose exterior sides form a straight line.

2. Through a given point *not* on a line, there exists exactly one perpendicular to the given line.

Complete each sentence below by filling in the blanks.

3. _____ angles are angles with measures that add to equal $180°$.

4. Vertical angles are a pair of _____ angles formed by two intersecting lines.

5. If two angles are supplementary to the same angle or equal (congruent) angles, then they are _____.

6. If the exterior sides of a pair of adjacent angles are perpendicular, the angles are _____.

Measure the distance below with a ruler (in inches).

7. the distance between point P and line n

From each given statement below, tell the definition, property, postulate, or theorem that justifies each prove statement.

8. Given: Lines $\overleftrightarrow{JK}$ and $\overleftrightarrow{LM}$ (shown at right) intersect at point N.
  Prove: $\angle JNM \cong \angle KNL$

9. Given: $\angle JNL$ and $\angle LNK$ are a linear pair.
  Prove: $\angle JNL$ and $\angle LNK$ are supplementary.

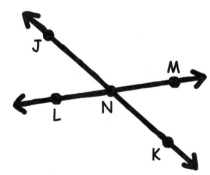

10. Given: $\angle X$ and $\angle Y$ are supplementary;
  $\angle Y$ and $\angle Z$ are supplementary.
  Prove: $\angle X \cong \angle Z$

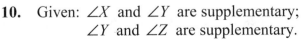

Find the measures of a complement and supplement of each angle below.

11. $m\angle PQR = 37$ **12.** $m\angle E = 90 - x$

Use the definition of a segment or angle bisector to answer each question below.

13. If $\overrightarrow{CE}$ bisects $\angle BCD$, and if $m\angle BCE = 3x - 6$ and $m\angle ECD = 2x + 11$ then find $m\angle BCD$. Is $\angle BCD$ acute, right, or obtuse?

14. If $\overrightarrow{IJ}$ bisects $\overline{GH}$ at point J, and if $GJ = 3y - 1$ and $JH = 2y + 7$, then find GH.

Tell whether each pair of angles below is adjacent. If a pair is not adjacent, briefly tell why not.

15.   **a.** $\angle RST$ and $\angle TSU$

        b. $\angle TSU$ and $\angle UVW$

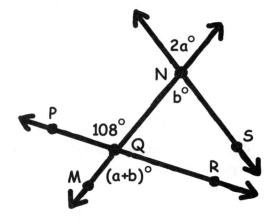

Find the measure of each angle below.

16. $\angle PQM$

17. $\angle QNS$

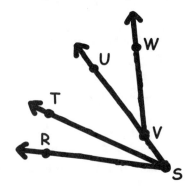

Write an equation to represent each question below; then solve the equation to get your answer.

18. An angle's measure is 18 more than three times its complement. Find the measure of the angle.

19. A supplement of an angle is 4 times as large as the angle's complement. Find the measure of the angle.

Complete the sentence below with *always*, *sometimes*, or *never*.

   20.   Adjacent angles are _____ supplementary.

Tell whether the arguments below are valid or invalid deductions.

   21.   If two angles are a linear pair, then they are supplementary. $\angle A$ and $\angle B$ are supplementary. Therefore, $\angle A$ and $\angle B$ are a linear pair.

   22.   Pairs of vertical angles are congruent. $\angle 1$ and $\angle 3$ are not congruent, so they are not a pair of vertical angles.

Complete the proof below by filling in the blanks.

   23.

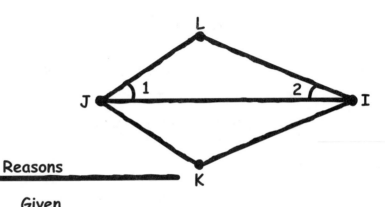

Given: $m\angle LIK = m\angle LJK$

        $\overline{IJ}$ bisects $\angle LIK$

        $\overline{IJ}$ bisects $\angle LJK$

Prove: $m\angle 1 = m\angle 2$

	Statements		Reasons
1.	$\overline{IJ}$ bisects $\angle LIK$	1.	Given
2.		2.	Given
3.	$m\angle 2 = \frac{1}{2}m\angle LIK$	3.	
4.		4.	Definition of angle bisector
5.	$m\angle LIK = m\angle LJK$	5.	
6.	$\frac{1}{2}m\angle LIK = \frac{1}{2}m\angle LJK$	6.	
7.		7.	Substitution Property

Do the proof below.

   24.   Given: $\angle 3$ is complementary to $\angle 1$,
                $\angle 4$ is complementary to $\angle 2$.
          Prove: $m\angle 1 = m\angle 2$

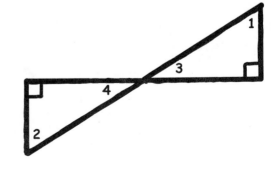

113

Chapter 4 Test

Tell whether each sentence below is True or False.

1. When the "if" clause and "then" clause of a statement are flipped around, the "converse" of the original statement is created.

2. If two parallel lines are cut by a transversal, then interior angles on the same side of the transversal are supplementary.

Complete each sentence below by filling in the blanks.

3. A(n) _____ is a line that intersects two or more lines in different points.

4. $\overrightarrow{EF} \parallel \overrightarrow{GH}$ means that _____.

5. If two lines form congruent alternate interior angles with a transversal, then the lines are _____.

6. A good definition is one where both the original statement and the _____ are true.

Tell whether each definition below passes the reversibility test by writing its converse and determining whether the converse is true.

7. If two angles are a linear pair, then the sum of their measures is 180°.

8. Parallel lines are lines that lie in the same plane and that never intersect.

Identify each pair of angles below as adjacent angles, vertical angles, alternate interior or exterior angles, corresponding angles, or supplementary angles. Tell whether each pair is congruent, supplementary, or neither.

9. ∠3 and ∠5

10. ∠2 and ∠6

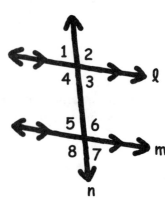

From each given statement below, tell the definition, property, postulate, or theorem that justifies each prove statement.

11. Given: $\ell \parallel m$; Prove: $\angle 3$ and $\angle 6$ are supplementary.

12. Given: $\angle 3 \cong \angle 5$; Prove: $\ell \parallel m$

13. Given: Lines m and n intersect; Prove: $\angle 5 \cong \angle 7$

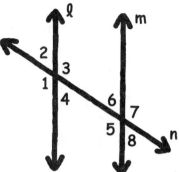

Complete each sentence below with *always*, *sometimes*, or *never*.

14. Corresponding angles are _____ congruent.

15. If two parallel lines are cut by a transversal, interior angles on the same side of the transversal are _____ supplementary.

Given $\ell \parallel m$, find the measure of each angle below.

16. $\angle PTU$ 17. $\angle QTP$

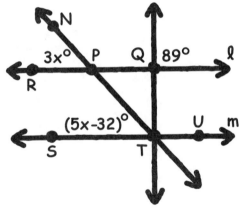

Write an equation to represent each question below; then solve the equation to get your answer.

18. $\angle W$ and $\angle Y$ are supplementary. If $m\angle W = 5x + 20$ and $m\angle Y = 4x - 11$, find $m\angle W$ and $m\angle Y$.

19. One angle of a linear pair is 10 more than two-thirds the other angle. Find *both* angles.

20. The difference between the measures of two complementary angles is 14. Find *both* angles.

Tell whether the arguments below are valid or invalid deductions.

21. If the two angles in a linear pair are equal, then each is a right angle. $\angle A$ and $\angle B$ are not right angles. Therefore, they are not an equal linear pair.

22. Parallel lines are lines that are coplanar and that never intersect. Lines ℓ and m never intersect. Therefore, $\ell \parallel m$.

Do each proof below.

23. Given: $\angle Q \cong \angle S$, $\overline{PQ} \parallel \overline{RS}$
Prove: $\overline{QR} \parallel \overline{ST}$

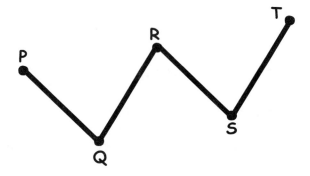

24. Given: $\overline{BC} \parallel \overline{AD}$, $\overline{AB} \parallel \overline{CD}$
Prove: $m\angle BCD = m\angle DAB$

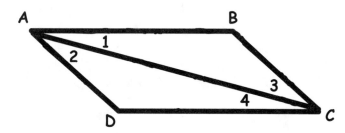

Chapter 5 Test

Tell whether each sentence below is True or False.

1. An exterior angle of a triangle (or any polygon) is complementary to its adjacent interior angle.

2. If triangles have two angles and one side congruent but the side is not between the angles, then the triangles are not necessarily congruent.

Complete each sentence below by filling in the blanks.

3. A scalene triangle has _____ congruent (equal) sides.

4. A(n) _____ triangle has two congruent (equal) sides.

5. The acute angles of a right triangle are _____.

6. The measure of an exterior angle of a triangle is _____ the sum of the measures of the _____ remote interior angles.

Answer question 7 based on the diagram at right.

7. What kind of triangle is ΔFGH with respect to its sides? What kind of triangle is it with respect to its angles?

Find the measures of the angles of the triangle described below.

8. A triangle whose angles have measures x, $x+30$, and $x-30$. What kind of triangle is it with respect to its angles?

From each given statement below, tell the definition, property, postulate, or theorem that justifies each prove statement.

9. Given: ΔSUV (at right); $m\angle S = 15$;
   $m\angle U = 50$
   Prove: $m\angle SVU = 115$

10. Given: ΔSUV and $\overrightarrow{ST}$ (at right)
    Prove: $m\angle UVT = m\angle S + m\angle U$

Complete each sentence below with *always*, *sometimes*, or *never*.

11. If a triangle is equilateral, then it is _____ isosceles.

12. An acute triangle _____ has an angle that is greater than $90°$.

Given $\triangle BCD \cong \triangle CBE$ in the diagram below, fill in each of the blanks.

13. $\overline{BC} \cong$ _____

   $\overline{BE} \cong$ _____

   $\angle DBC \cong$ _____

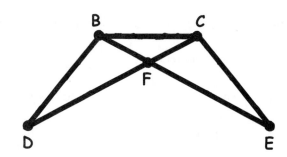

From the diagram at right, name a pair of lines that must be parallel if the statement below is true. If there are no lines that have to be parallel, write "none" for your answer.

14. $\angle 4 \cong \angle 7$

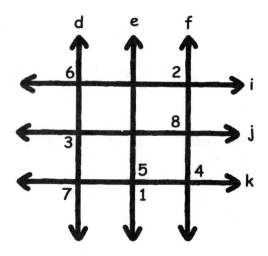

Answer each question below.

15. In $\triangle ABC$, the exterior angle adjacent to $\angle C$ measures $120°$. If $m\angle A = 2x$ and $m\angle B = x + 15$, find the measures of the angles of $\triangle ABC$.

16. If $\triangle JKL \cong \triangle QRS$, list all of the congruent sides from the two triangles.

Answer each question below.

17. Find *x* and *y*.

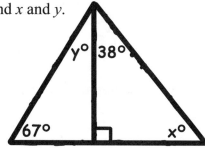

18. Find *y*.

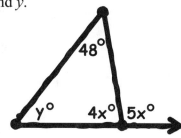

19. Find *x*.

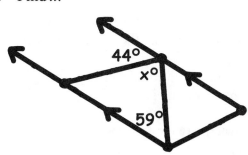

20. Find *x* and *y*.

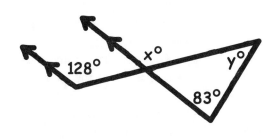

Write the converse of each statement below. Tell whether the converse is True or False.

21. If two triangles are congruent, then all three pairs of their sides are congruent.

22. If a triangle is a right triangle, then it has two acute angles.

Do each proof below.

23. Given: $\overline{JK} \perp \overline{KL}$, $\overline{JM} \perp \overline{ML}$,
$\angle KJL \cong \angle MJL$
Prove: $\triangle JKL \cong \triangle JML$

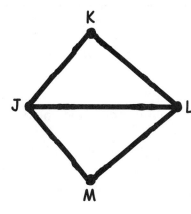

24. Given: $\overline{AF} \perp \overline{BD}$, $\overline{CE} \perp \overline{BD}$,
$AB = CD$, $BE = FD$
Prove: $\triangle ABF \cong \triangle CDE$

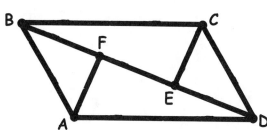

Chapter 6 Test

Tell whether each sentence below is True or False.

1. The Converse Base Angles Theorem can be used to prove that a triangle is isosceles.

2. C.P.C.T.C. is a shortcut for proving that two triangles are congruent.

Complete each sentence below by filling in the blanks.

3. A(n) _____ of a triangle is a segment drawn from any vertex of the triangle, perpendicular to the opposite side, extended outside the triangle if necessary.

4. The measure of an exterior angle of a triangle is equal to the _____ of the measures of the two _____ interior angles.

5. According to the _____ shortcut, two triangles are congruent if all three of their corresponding sides are congruent.

Answer each question below based on the accompanying diagram.

6. Which angles of $\triangle IGH$ are congruent?

7. Which sides of $\triangle FGI$ are congruent?

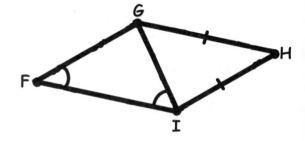

Draw each line segment described below.

8. Draw the altitude of $\triangle JKL$ from vertex J.

9. Draw the median of $\triangle JKL$ from vertex K.

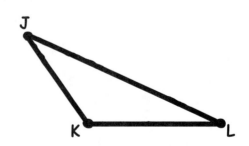

State which shortcut can be used to prove each pair of triangles below congruent. If no method applies, say "none."

10.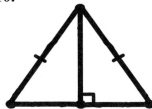

11.

12.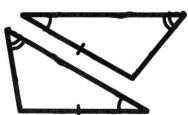

Find the measures of the angles of the triangle described below.

13. An isosceles triangle with a vertex angle of 88°.

From each given statement below, tell the definition, property, postulate, or theorem that justifies each prove statement.

14. Given: $\angle LIK \cong \angle IKJ$
Prove: $\overline{IL} \parallel \overline{JK}$

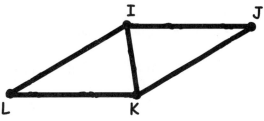

15. Given: $\triangle PQR$ and $\angle P \cong \angle Q$
Prove: $\overline{PR} \cong \overline{RQ}$

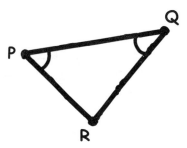

Answer each question below.

16. Find x.

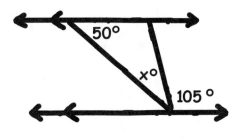

17. Find x and y.

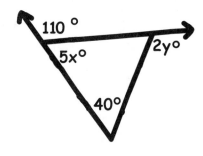

18. Find x and y.

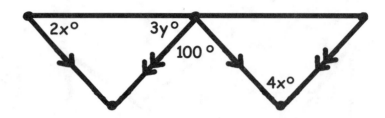

Write an equation to represent each question below; then solve the equation to get your answer.

19. An angle is equal to one-third its complement. Find the angle's measure.

20. Two angles are a linear pair. The measure of the first angle minus 39 is equal to twice the measure of the second angle. What are the measures of *both* angles?

Write the converse of each statement below. Tell whether the converse is True or False.

21. If a triangle is obtuse, then it has one angle that is greater than $90°$.

22. If two angles of a triangle are congruent (equal), then the sides opposite those angles are congruent (equal).

Do each proof below.

23. Given: $\overline{KM} \parallel \overline{JH}$, $\overline{KM} \cong \overline{JH}$, $\overline{JK} \cong \overline{KL}$
Prove: $\overline{HK} \parallel \overline{ML}$

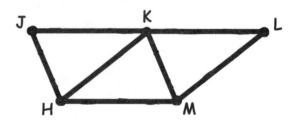

24. Given: $\triangle ABC$; $\overline{CA} \cong \overline{CB}$;
altitudes $\overline{AD}$ and $\overline{BE}$
Prove: $\overline{AD} \cong \overline{BE}$

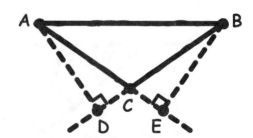

Chapter 7 Test

Tell whether each sentence below is true or false.

1. The sum of the lengths of any two sides of a triangle must be less than the length of the remaining side.

2. A statement is always logically equivalent to its contrapositive.

Complete each sentence below by filling in the blanks.

3. When _____ or _____ both sides of an inequality by a negative number, the inequality symbol must be flipped.

4. If the original statement is in the form "If a, then b," then the converse is in the form _____.

5. If the original statement is in the form "If a, then b," then the contrapositive is in the form _____.

6. If the original statement is in the form "If a, then b," then the inverse is in the form _____.

Tell whether each set of numbers below can represent the side lengths of a triangle.

7. a. 5, 8, 14   b. 12, 16, 20

The lengths of two sides of a triangle are given. Tell the lengths that the third side must be greater than and less than.

8. a. 7, 2   b. 12, 21

Solve each inequality below. Show your steps and give a reason for each one.

9. $6x + 23 > -2x + 7$ 10. $-\dfrac{1}{2}y - 1 \le 3$

Find the measures of the angles of each triangle described below.

11. An isosceles obtuse triangle with one angle measuring $32°$.

12. A right triangle where one of the two acute angles measures 8 times the other.

Write the converse, inverse, and contrapositive of each true statement below. Tell whether your answer is true or false.

13. If Mike lives in Honolulu, then he lives in Hawaii.

14. If two angles are both right angles, then they are congruent.

From each given statement below, tell the definition, property, postulate, or theorem that justifies each prove statement.

15. Given: $\triangle DEF$; Prove: $EF + FD > DE$

16. Given: $\triangle DEF$; Prove: $\angle GEF > \angle F$

17. Given: $\angle DFE > \angle DEF$; Prove: $DE > DF$

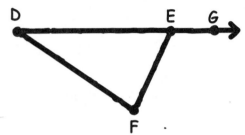

Answer question 18 based on the diagram at right

18. In $\triangle IJK$, $IJ = 4$ and $JK = 6$. Is $\angle I$ or $\angle K$ greater?

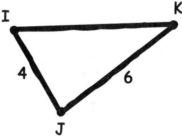

Answer each question below.

19. Find $m + n$.

20. $\triangle MNO$ is equilateral. Find x and y.

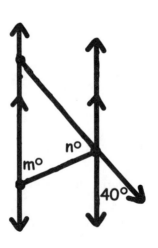

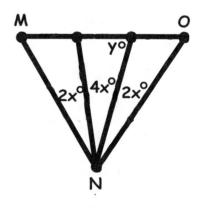

21. Find *x*.

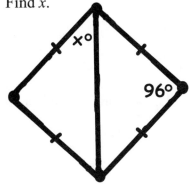

22. Find *a*.

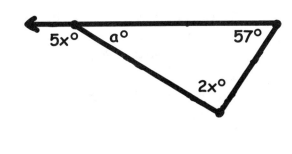

Do each proof below. Use the indirect method on 24.

23. Given: $\overline{PQ} \cong \overline{PR}$, $\overline{QR} \parallel \overline{ST}$
Prove: $\triangle SPT$ is isosceles.

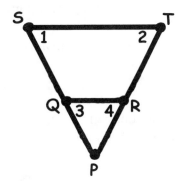

24. Given: $IJ = KJ$
Prove: $IL \neq LM$

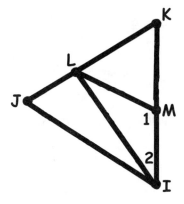

Chapter 8 Test

Tell whether each sentence below is True or False.

1. Consecutive pairs of angles of a parallelogram are congruent.

2. If both pairs of opposite sides are congruent, then a quadrilateral is a parallelogram.

Complete each sentence below by filling in the blanks.

3. The sum of the measures of the angles of any quadrilateral is _____.

4. A _____ is a quadrilateral that has one pair of opposite sides parallel.

5. The _____ of a parallelogram bisect each other.

6. The line segment joining the midpoints of two sides of a triangle is _____ to the third side and _____ its length.

Tell whether each figure below is a trapezoid, isosceles trapezoid, parallelogram, rectangle, rhombus, square, or just a plain quadrilateral.

7.
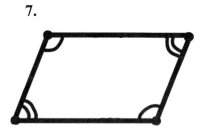

8.
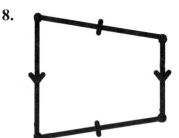

9.
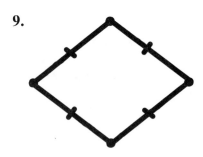

Complete each sentence below with *always*, *sometimes*, or *never*.

10. A rhombus is _____ a parallelogram.

11. Pairs of consecutive angles of a parallelogram are _____ congruent.

Write the converse, inverse, and contrapositive of each true statement below. Tell whether your answer is true or false.

12. If a figure is a rhombus, then it is a parallelogram.

13. If a figure is not a rectangle, then it is not a square.

From each given statement below, tell the definition, property, postulate, or theorem that justifies each prove statement.

14. Given: Rhombus *RSTU*
Prove: $\overline{RT} \perp \overline{SU}$

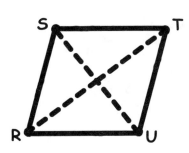

15. Given: Isosceles trapezoid *MNOP*
Prove: $\overline{MO} \cong \overline{PN}$

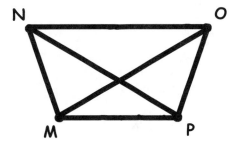

16. Given: Quadrilateral *IJKL*,
$\overline{IJ} \parallel \overline{LK}$, $\overline{IJ} \cong \overline{LK}$
Prove: *IJKL* is a parallelogram.

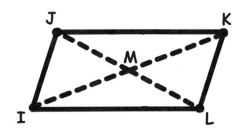

Answer each question below.

17. Find *x*, *y*, and *z*.

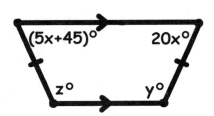

18. Find *x*.

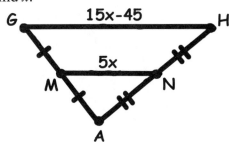

19. Find y.

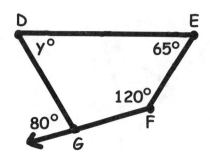

20. In parallelogram *RSWY*, find $m\angle R$ and $m\angle S$.

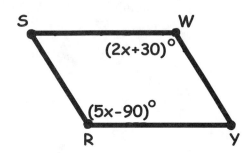

Answer each question below.

21. In $\triangle FGH$, $FG = 8.7$, $FH = 4.5$ and $GH = 6.1$. Which is the smallest angle of the triangle?

22. In $\triangle JKL$, $m\angle J = 40$ and $m\angle L$ is three times $m\angle K$. Find $m\angle K$ and $m\angle L$.

Do each proof below.

23. Given: Rectangle *EJHG*, $\overline{JI} \cong \overline{FG}$
Prove: $\overline{EI} \cong \overline{HF}$

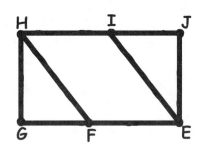

24. Given: $\triangle NOP \cong \triangle QRP$,
    N is the midpoint of $\overline{MO}$.
Prove: *MNQR* is a parallelogram.

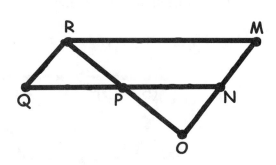

Chapter 9 Test

Tell whether each sentence below is True or False.

1. The number of angles of a polygon is equal to the number of its sides.

2. A regular polygon is a convex polygon where every one of its sides is congruent and every one of its interior angles is congruent.

Complete each sentence below by filling in the blanks.

3. A 5-sided polygon is called a _____, and a 6-sided polygon is called a _____.

4. The measure of each exterior angle of a regular polygon equals _____.

5. The sum of the measures of the interior angles of a polygon with n sides is _____.

Name the type of each polygon below and tell whether it's convex or concave.

6.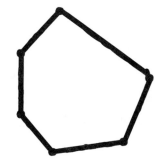

7.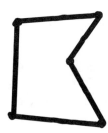

8.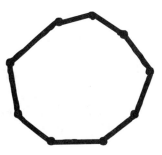

Draw all of the diagonals in each polygon below and tell how many diagonals there are.

9.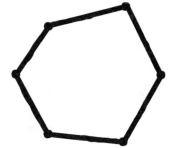

10.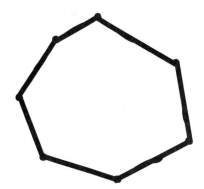

Name each regular polygon below and find the measure of the interior angle and exterior angle indicated.

11.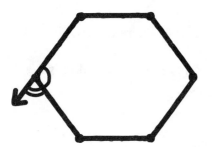

12.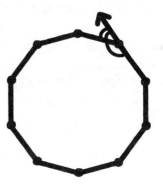

Find the sum of the exterior angles of the polygon below.

13.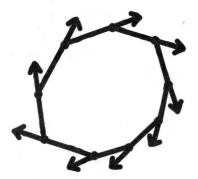

Complete each sentence below with *always*, *sometimes*, or *never*.

14. A regular polygon is _____ convex.

15. The sum of the measures of all the exterior angles of a polygon is _____ equal to 180.

Write the converse, inverse, and contrapositive of each true statement below. Tell whether your answer is true or false.

16. If a figure is a regular polygon, then it is equilateral.

Find the perimeter of each polygon described below.

17. A rectangle with length measuring 14 and width measuring 3.

18. A regular nonagon with sides measuring 14.

Answer each question below.

19. Find $x + y$.

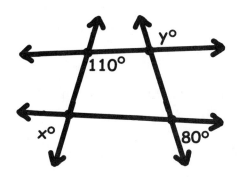

20. Find x.

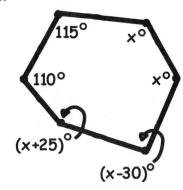

21. Find $a + b + c + d$.

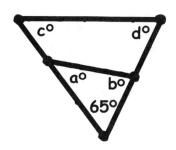

22. In rectangle *IJKL*, find x and y.

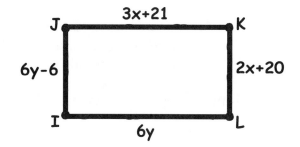

Do each proof below.

23. Given: *GCDE* is a rectangle;
        GCEF is a parallelogram.
    Prove: $\triangle GDF$ is isosceles.

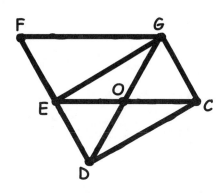

24. Given: *PQRS* is a parallelogram.
        $\overline{TQ} \perp \overline{QR}$, $\overline{US} \perp \overline{PS}$
    Prove: $\triangle PQT \cong \triangle RSU$

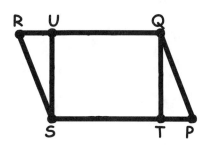

Chapter 10 Test

Tell whether each sentence below is True or False.

1. If $\triangle FGH \sim \triangle QRS$, then $\dfrac{SQ}{HF} = \dfrac{RS}{GH}$.

2. If one angle and one side of a triangle are congruent to a corresponding angle and side of another triangle, then the triangles are similar.

Complete each sentence below by filling in the blanks.

3. A _____ is two ratios that are set equal to each other.

4. If a line is _____ to one side of a triangle and intersects the other two sides, then the line divides those sides proportionally.

5. If two triangles are _____, then their vertices can be paired in a correspondence so that all pairs of corresponding angles are congruent and all pairs of corresponding sides are proportional.

Tell whether each pair of ratios below is equal.

6. **a.** $\dfrac{4}{9}, \dfrac{20}{45}$ **b.** $63:27,\ 14:6$ **c.** 11 to 44, 44 to 11

Solve the proportion below by cross-multiplying.

7. Solve for r in $\dfrac{r}{r+15} = \dfrac{3}{8}$.

Find the geometric mean of the pair of numbers below.

8. Find the geometric mean of 2 and 32.

In the triangle below, find each of the ratios indicated. Do the ratios show that the sides are divided proportionally?

9. $\dfrac{IL}{JL}$ and $\dfrac{IM}{KM}$

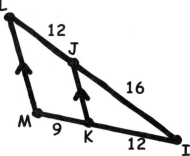

Write a proportion to represent each question below; then solve the proportion to get your answer.

10. The garage on a house blueprint measures 4 inches wide and 6 inches long. If the actual garage is going to have a length of 45 feet, what will its width be?

11. The ratio of the corresponding sides of two similar quadrilaterals is $7 : 4$. If the length of the longest side of the larger quadrilateral is 56 cm, find the length of the longest side of the smaller quadrilateral.

From each given statement below, tell the definition, property, postulate, or theorem that justifies each prove statement.

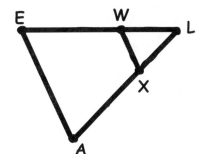

12. Given: $\dfrac{WL}{EL} = \dfrac{XL}{AL} = \dfrac{XW}{AE}$

Prove: $\triangle AEL \sim \triangle XWL$

13. Given $\triangle ELA \sim \triangle WLX$

Prove: $\dfrac{EL}{WL} = \dfrac{AL}{XL}$

Use proportions to tell whether the pair of figures below is similar.

14.

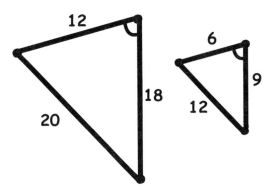

State which shortcut can be used to prove that each pair of triangles below are similar. If no method applies, say "none."

15.

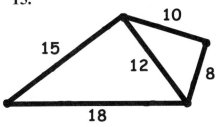

16.

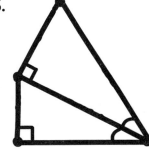

17.

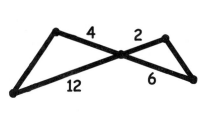

Answer each question below.

18. If $\triangle EIF \sim \triangle GIH$, find the perimeter of $\triangle GIH$.

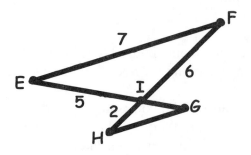

19. If *PQRS* is a rhombus, find *y*.

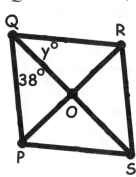

20. Find *y*.

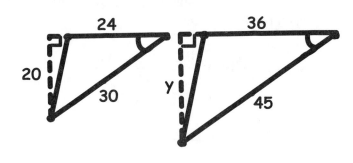

21. Assume $\triangle MNO \sim \triangle PQR$. If the perimeter of $\triangle MNO$ is 48, the perimeter of $\triangle PQR$ is 12, $MO = 12x$, and $PR = x + 2$, find *MO* and *PR*.

22. Assume $\triangle IJK \sim \triangle PQR$ with medians $\overline{IM}$ and $\overline{PN}$ to sides $\overline{JK}$ and $\overline{QR}$ respectively, $IJ = 15$, and $PQ = 9$. If *IM* is 2 greater than *PN*, find both medians.

Do each proof below.

23. Given: $\overline{MN} \cong \overline{NO}$, $\overline{GH} \perp \overline{MO}$, $\overline{PQ} \perp \overline{MO}$
Prove: $\triangle GHO \sim \triangle PQM$

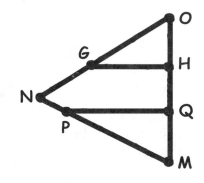

24. Given: $\triangle ORC \sim \triangle FEH$;
$\overline{RT}$ bisects $\angle ORC$;
$\overline{EG}$ bisects $\angle FEH$
Prove: $\triangle RTC \sim \triangle EGH$

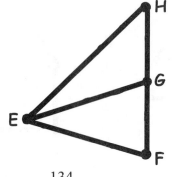

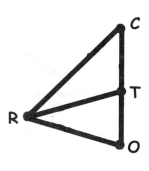

134

Chapter 11 Test

Tell whether each sentence below is True or False.

1. According to the Pythagorean Theorem, in any right triangle the square of the two legs added together equals the square of the hypotenuse.

2. The cosine ratio for a particular angle in a right triangle is the opposite side to that angle divided by the hypotenuse.

Complete each sentence below by filling in the blanks.

3. The tangent ratio for a particular angle in a right triangle is the _____ side to that angle divided by the _____ side.

4. The altitude to the hypotenuse of a right triangle forms two triangles that are _____ to each other and to the original triangle.

5. A _____ is three whole numbers that can be the side lengths of a right triangle.

Simplify each irrational number below, then estimate it to two decimal places.

6. $\sqrt{75}$

7. $\sqrt{128}$

Tell whether each set of numbers below is a Pythagorean Triple

8. $\{15, 20, 25\}$

9. $\{6, 9, 12\}$

Find the missing lengths in the right triangles below.

10. Find x.

11. Find x.

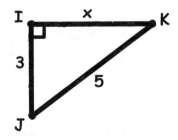

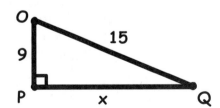

Use proportions or the Pythagorean Theorem to find the missing values below. Estimate your answer to 2 decimal places.

12. Find x.

13. Find y.

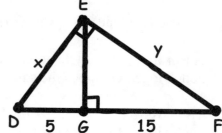

Calculate each trigonometric ratio below. Estimate your answers to 2 decimal places.

14. $\tan 25°$ **15.** $\sin 65°$

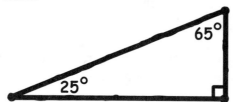

Use the tangent ratio to find the missing leg of each right triangle below. Estimate your answers to 2 decimal places.

16.

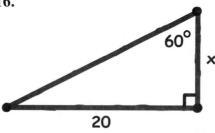

17.

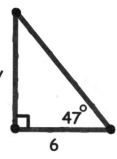

Answer each question below.

18. A basketball hoop is 10 feet high. If Steve is 5 feet tall, and standing 12 feet away from the hoop, what is the distance from the top of Steve's head to the hoop?.

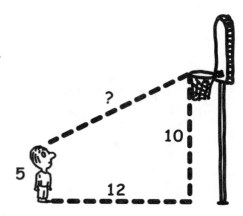

19. Find *x*.

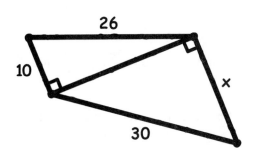

20. Find *y*.

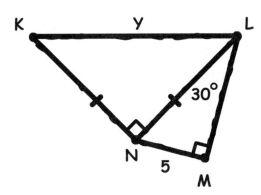

Write an equation to represent each question below; then solve the equation to get your answer.

21. Fiona is standing 26 meters from the base of an oak tree. If she measures the angle of elevation to the top of the tree to be 37°, how tall is the tree? Estimate your answer to 2 decimal places.

22. A plane veered off its course at an angle of 11°. If the plane ended up 170 miles due west of its planned destination, how far did it fly? Estimate your answer to 2 decimal places.

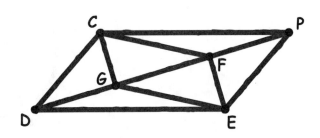

Do each proof below.

23. Given: $\triangle FCE \sim \triangle HID$;
$\overline{GD}$ bisects $\angle IDF$
Prove: $\triangle FCE \sim \triangle HCD$

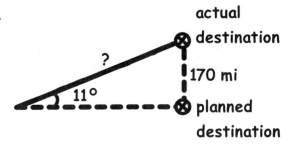

24. Given: *PCDE* is a parallelogram;
$\overline{PF} \cong \overline{DG}$
Prove: *FCGE* is a parallelogram.

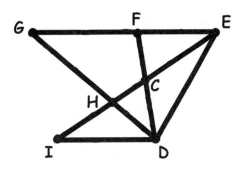

137

Chapter 12 Test

Tell whether each sentence below is True or False.

1. If a radius is drawn to the point of tangency of a tangent line, then the radius is perpendicular to the tangent line.

2. An inscribed angle is equal in measure to the measure of its intercepted arc.

Complete each sentence below by filling in the blanks.

3. A _____ line is a line which intersects a circle in two different points.

4. An inscribed angle that intercepts a _____ is a right angle.

5. The measure of an angle formed by two chords (or secants) intersecting in the interior of a circle is equal to one-half the _____ of the measures of the two intercepted arcs.

Tell whether each of the following parts of circle O is a radius, diameter, chord, tangent line, or secant line.

6. $\overleftrightarrow{EF}$

7. $\overline{MN}$

8. $\overline{QO}$

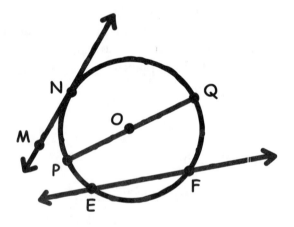

Find the degree measure of each arc or central angle indicated below.

9. $\angle EOF$

10. $\overarc{DGF}$

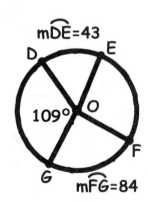

138

Find the linear measure of each arc indicated below.

11. $\widehat{PQ}$

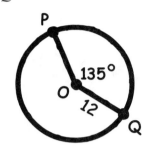

12. $\widehat{TSU}$

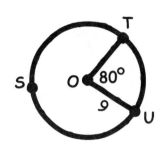

Find the degree measure of each arc or angle below.

13. $\angle IMJ$

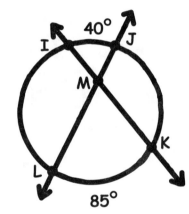

14. $\angle DPR$

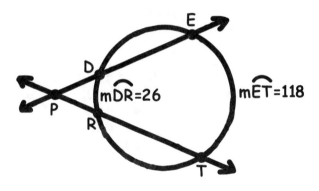

Find each missing line segment indicated below.

15. Find *IM.*

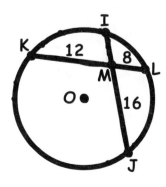

16. Find *ST.*

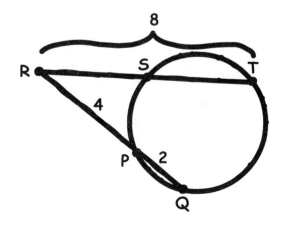

Answer each question below.

17. Find *x*.

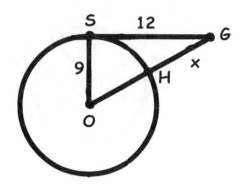

18. Find *y*.

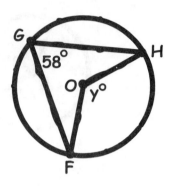

19. If QR is tangent to $\odot O$, find *x*.

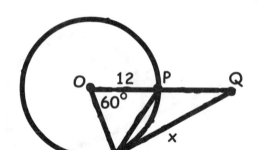

20. If $m\widehat{DE} = 50$, find *d*.

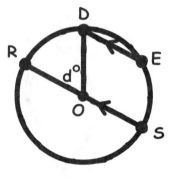

From each given statement below, tell the definition, property, postulate, or theorem that justifies each prove statement.

21. Given: $\overline{AC} \perp \overline{OB}$
Prove: $\overline{AG} \cong \overline{GC}$

22. Given: $\overline{OG} \cong \overline{OF}$
Prove: $\overline{AC} \cong \overline{DE}$

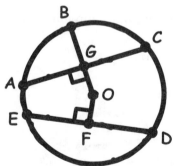

Do each proof below.

23. Given: $\overline{IK}$ and $\overline{IM}$ are secant segments;
$IK = IM$
Prove: $IJ = IL$

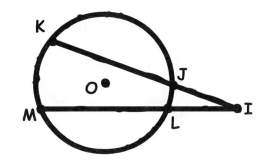

24. Given: $\overline{PQ} \perp \overline{RS}$
Prove: $\overset{\frown}{RP} \cong \overset{\frown}{PS}$

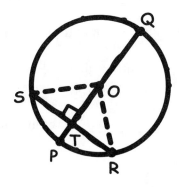

Chapter 13 Test

Tell whether each sentence below is True or False.

1. The area of a parallelogram is equal to one-half the product of the base and the altitude.

2. A segment of a circle is a region of a circle bounded by a chord and the minor arc that it intercepts.

Complete each sentence below by filling in the blanks.

3. The area of a rhombus is equal to one-half the product of _____.

4. If two polygons are similar, then the ratio of their areas is equal to the _____ of the ratio of the lengths of any two corresponding sides.

5. The area of a _____ is equal to one-half the product of the base and the altitude.

Calculate the area of each rectangle described below.

6. A rectangle with a base of 15 inches and an altitude of 7 inches.

7. A rectangle with an altitude of 30 cm and a diagonal of 50 cm.

Calculate the area of each figure below.

8. $\triangle PQR$ **9.** $\triangle IJK$ **10.** $\square MNOP$

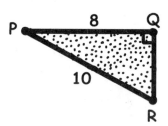

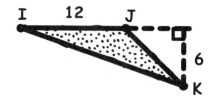

Calculate the area of each figure below.

11.

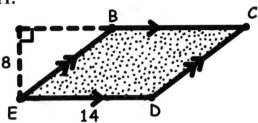
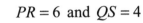

12.

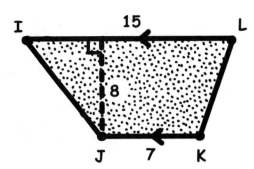

13. $PR = 6$ and $QS = 4$

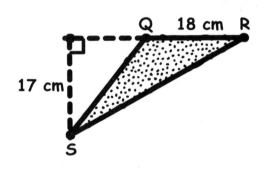

14.

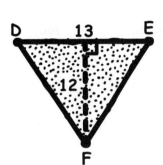

Calculate the area of each figure below.

15. $\triangle QRS$

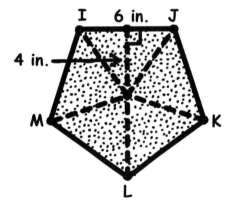

16. Regular pentagon *IJKLM*

17. $\square WXYZ$

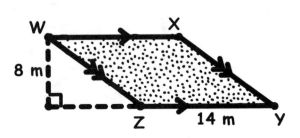

18. Trapezoid BCDE

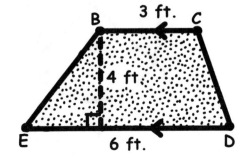

Calculate the area of each shaded region below.

19.

20.

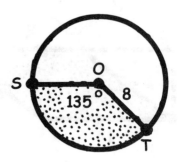

Write an equation to represent each question below; then solve the equation to get your answer.

21. In $\triangle TUV$, $\angle T$ is a right angle, $TU = 10$, $UV = 26$, and $VT = 24$. If $\triangle TUV \sim \triangle WXY$ and $WY = 72$, what is the area of $\triangle WXY$?

22. If the area of $PQRS = 60$, find x.

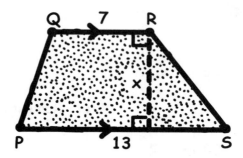

Do each proof below.

23. Given: $\overline{LK} \cong \overline{IJ}$
   Prove: $\overline{LJ} \cong \overline{IK}$

24. Given: $\overrightarrow{PR}$ is tangent to $\odot O$ at P;
   $\overrightarrow{QR}$ is tangent to $\odot O$ at Q
   Prove: $\overrightarrow{RS}$ bisects $\angle PRQ$.

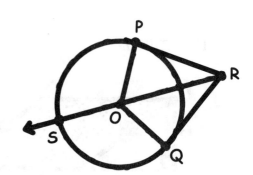

Chapter 14 Test

Tell whether each sentence below is True or False.

1. The total (surface) area of a rectangular solid is its length times its width times its altitude.

2. The volume and surface area of a sphere can both be calculated if you know only the radius of the sphere.

Complete each sentence below by filling in the blanks.

3. The volume of a prism equals the product of the _____ and the _____.

4. The total area of a prism is equal to the product of the _____ and the _____ of a base plus 2 times the _____.

5. The volume of a cone is equal to _____ times the area of the base times the altitude, but since the base is a circle, the formula is written as _____.

Calculate the area of each shaded region below.

6.

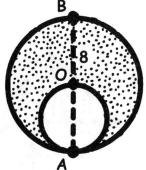

7.

8.

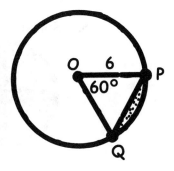

Calculate the surface area and volume of each rectangular solid below.

9.

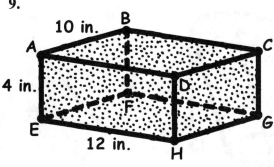

10.

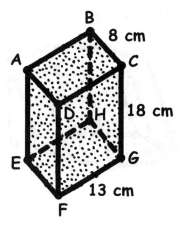

Identify each solid below.

11.

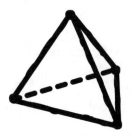

12.

Calculate the total area of each prism below.

13. Perimeter of base = 24;
Area of base = 30

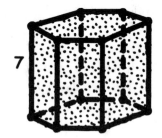

14. Base is a regular pentagon;
Area of base = 50

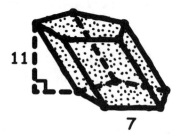

Calculate the total area of each solid below.

15. Sphere

16. Base is a square.

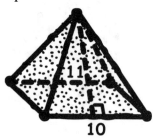

Calculate the volume of each solid described below.

17. Area of base = 707

18.

19. Base is a regular pentagon
of area 35. Altitude = 9.

Answer each question below.

20. If the area of the sector is 40π, find n.

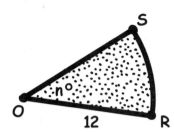

21. Find c.

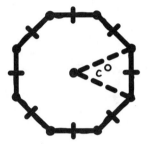

22. The edges of a large cube are 4 times as long as the edges of a smaller, similar cube. What is the ratio of the volume of the large cube to the volume of the small cube?

Do each proof below.

23. Given: $\overline{KL} \parallel \overline{IJ}$
   Prove: $\overset{\frown}{IK} \cong \overset{\frown}{JL}$

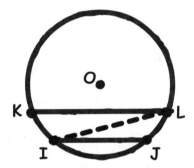

24. Given: A regular polygon
   Prove: An apothem of the polygon bisects a side of the polygon.

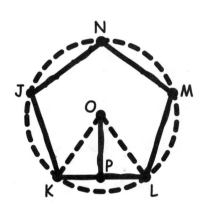

Chapter 15 Test

Tell whether each sentence below is True or False.

1. The distance (d) between points (x_1, y_1) and (x_2, y_2) may be found with the formula $d = \sqrt{(x_2 + x_1)^2 - (y_2 + y_1)^2}$.

2. The point-slope form of a linear equation is $y - y_0 = m(x - x_0)$, where m is the slope and (x_0, y_0) is any point on the line.

Complete each sentence below by filling in the blanks.

3. Each point on a coordinate plane can be represented by a pair of numbers called the _____ and _____ of the point.

4. If the slopes of two nonvertical lines are _____ of one another, then the lines are perpendicular.

5. The slope-intercept form of a linear equation is _____, where m is the _____ and b is the y-coordinate of the _____ of the line.

Find the missing coordinates of the points on each diagram below.

6. Rectangle *EFGH*

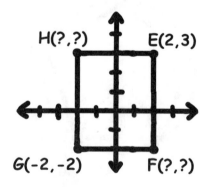

7. Isosceles right triangle *OPQ*

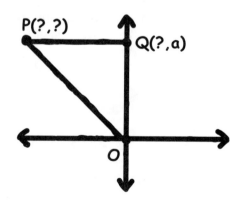

Calculate the area of each shaded region below.

8. *JIK* is a semicircle.

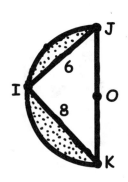

9. Parallelogram *ORST*

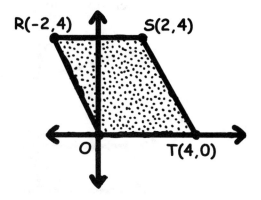

Find the midpoint of each line segment below.

10. $\overline{DE}$

11. $\overline{UV}$

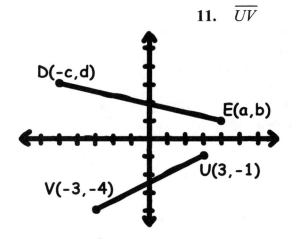

Find the lengths of the dashed sides of each diagram below.

12. Parallelogram *OWSD*

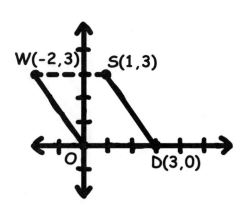

13. Right triangle *OPQ*

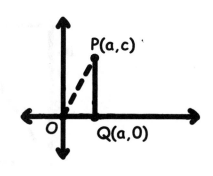

Answer each question below.

14. List the lines below in order by their slopes from least to greatest.

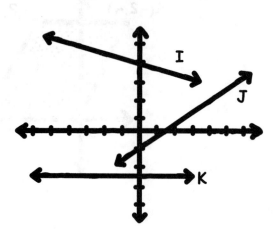

15. Calculate the slopes of lines E and F.

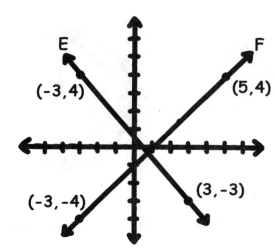

16. A right prism has an altitude of 16 cm and a base that is a right triangle with legs measuring 3 cm and 4 cm. Find the total area of a similar right prism that has a base whose legs measure 6 cm and 8 cm.

17. What is the volume of a right pyramid that has an altitude of 18 and a base which is a rhombus with diagonals measuring 10 and 24.

Write the equation for each line described below.

18. The line crossing the point $(-3, 8)$ and with slope -1.

19. The line that crosses the point $(2, -5)$ and is perpendicular to the line $y = \frac{2}{3}x + 4$.

Answer each question below.

20. *PRSU* and *PQWV* are squares. Find y.

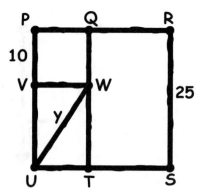

21. *IJKL* is a square with an area of 36. Find r.

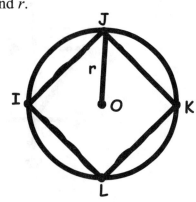

150

22. Find *r* in terms of *x*, *y*, *m*, and *n*.

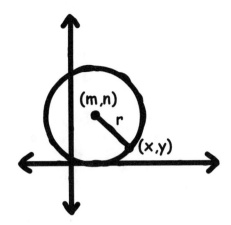

Do the coordinate proof below.

23. Given: Quadrilateral *PQRS*
    with coordinates as shown
  Prove: $PS = QR$ and $PQ = SR$

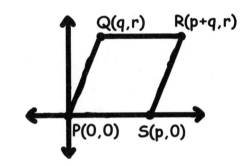

Do the proof below.

24. Given: $\overline{HJ} \parallel \overline{FG}$
  Prove: $\overline{JE} \cong \overline{HE}$

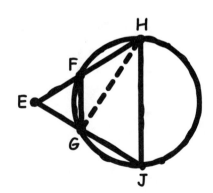

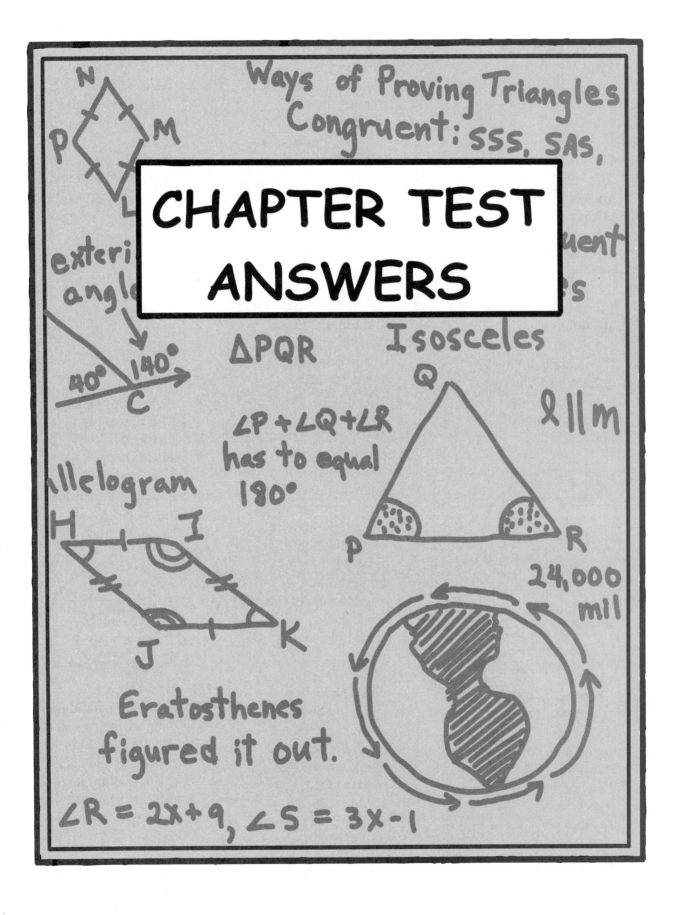

N

P

M

L

Ways of Proving Triangles Congruent: SSS, SAS,

CHAPTER TEST ANSWERS

exteri

angle

40° 140°

C

ΔPQR

∠P + ∠Q + ∠R
has to equal
180°

Isosceles

Q

P

R

ℓ || m

uent
es

24,000
mil

llelogram

H

I

J

K

Eratosthenes
figured it out.

∠R = 2x + 9, ∠S = 3x - 1

Chapter 1 Test

1. True
2. False
3. False
4. B
5. E
6. D
7. The vaccine will always
8. always equal to 2 inches
9. Premise: If a team has only an inch to go on fourth down; Conclusion: then they absolutely must go for it.
10. If you are a runaway grocery cart, then you hate it when the parking lot slopes upward.
11.

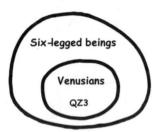

12.

13. If a city is in Kenya, then it is in Africa. If Nairobi is in Kenya, then it is in Africa.
14. If an orchestra member plays the triangle, then he definitely feels underappreciated. If Lester is the orchestra's triangle player, then he definitely feels underappreciated.
15. Deductive
16. Inductive
17. Invalid
18. Valid
19. then he better become a slugger.
20. Jumbo is afraid of mice.
21. shined his flash-light in the faces
22. Theorem: If the scoop falls off the cone, the driver will hit the fire hydrant.
23. If the bride stares for too long into the groom's eyes, she will delay the cutting of the cake by half an hour. If the cake-cutting is delayed by half an hour, then Brenda, one of the bridesmaids, will have to leave early. If Brenda leaves early, she will not catch the bouquet. If she does not catch the bouquet, Brenda won't get married next.
24. If Mom drops her pots and pans, they will hit the floor. If the pots and pans hit the floor, the baby will begin to cry. If the baby begins to cry, the dog will start to bark. If the dog starts to bark, all the neighbors will wake up.

Chapter 2 Test

1. False
2. True
3. False
4. plane
5. bisector
6. vertex
7. Two points
8. multiplied; equal; Multiplication Property
9. substituted; Substitution Property
10. **a.** line segment; **b.** angle; **c.** ray
11. two; one; none
12.

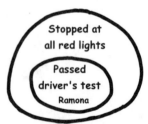

13. If you are a true mountain man, then your beard goes all the way down to your chest. If Travis is a true mountain man, then his beard goes all the way down to his chest.

14. $\overrightarrow{CA}$ is between $\overrightarrow{CB}$ and $\overrightarrow{CD}$.
15. $LM = 7\dfrac{3}{4}$
16. $PV = 14.6$
17. $m\angle MNP = 134$
18. $\angle FJH$ (or $\angle HJF$); $27°$, acute
19. Valid
20. Invalid
21. she can shatter glass with her voice
22. If the explorer's hunch is wrong, then his map will be off by 1,000 miles.
   If his map is off by 1,000 miles, he and his crew will run out of food before they reach the islands.
   If they run out of food before they reach the islands, they will all begin to starve.
   If they all begin to starve, he and the crew will end up eating shoe leather for breakfast.
23. A famous artist was Michelangelo; does not pass
24. A sandwich containing only bacon, lettuce, and tomato is a BLT; passes

Chapter 3 Test
1. False
2. True
3. Supplementary
4. nonadjacent

5. equal (congruent)
6. complementary
7. approximately $1\dfrac{1}{8}$ inches
8. Pairs of vertical angles are congruent.
9. If two angles are a linear pair, then they are supplementary.
10. If two angles are supplementary to the same angle, then they are congruent.
11. complement: $53°$ supplement: $143°$
12. complement: x supplement: $90 + x$
13. $m\angle BCD = 90$; right
14. $GH = 46$
15. **a.** Adjacent; **b.** Not adjacent; don't have the same vertex
16. $m\angle PQM = 72$
17. $m\angle QNS = 72$
18. $72°$
19. $60°$
20. sometimes
21. Invalid
22. Valid
23. (2) $\overline{IJ}$ bisects $\angle LJK$.
   (3) Definition of angle bisector
   (4) $m\angle 1 = \frac{1}{2} m\angle LJK$
   (5) Given

(6) Multiplication Property
(7) $m\angle 1 = m\angle 2$
24. (1) $\angle 3$ is complementary to $\angle 1$.(Given)
   (2) $\angle 4$ is complementary to $\angle 2$.(Given)
   (3) $m\angle 3 = m\angle 4$ (Pairs of vertical angles are equal.)
   (4) $m\angle 1 = m\angle 2$ (If two angles are complementary to equal angles, then they are equal.)

Chapter 4 Test
1. True
2. True
3. transversal
4. lines EF and GH are parallel
5. parallel
6. converse
7. If the sum of the measures of two angles is $180°$, then the angles form a linear pair.; Converse is not true; definition does not pass
8. Lines that lie in the same plane and that never intersect are parallel lines.; Converse is true; definition does pass
9. alternate interior angles; congruent
10. corresponding angles; congruent
11. If two parallel lines are cut by a transversal, then interior

angles on the same side of the transversal are supplementary.

12. If two lines form congruent alternate interior angles with a transversal, then the lines are parallel.

13. Pairs of vertical angles are congruent.

14. sometimes

15. always

16. 132°

17. 43°

18. $m\angle W = 115$; $m\angle Y = 65$

19. 102°, 78°

20. 52°, 38°

21. Valid

22. Invalid

23. **(1)** $\angle Q \cong \angle S$, $\overline{PQ} \| \overline{RS}$ (Given)
 (2) $\angle Q \cong \angle R$ (If two parallel lines are cut by a transversal, then their alternate interior angles are congruent.)
 (3) $\angle R \cong \angle S$ (Transitive or Substitution)
 (4) $\overline{QR} \| \overline{ST}$ (If two lines form congruent alternate interior angles with a transversal, then the lines are parallel.)

24. **(1)** $\overline{BC} \| \overline{AD}$, $\overline{AB} \| \overline{CD}$ (Given)
 (2) $m\angle 3 = m\angle 2$, $m\angle 4 = m\angle 1$ (If two parallel lines are cut by a transversal, then alternate interior angles are equal.)

(3) $m\angle 3 + m\angle 4 = m\angle 2 + m\angle 1$ (Addition)
 (4) $m\angle BCD = m\angle 3 + m\angle 4$ and $m\angle DAB = m\angle 1 + m\angle 2$ (Betweenness of Rays)
 (5) $m\angle BCD = m\angle DAB$ (Substitution)

Chapter 5 Test

1. False
2. False
3. no
4. isosceles
5. complementary
6. equal to; two
7. Scalene; obtuse
8. 60°, 90°, 30°; right
9. The sum of the measures of the angles of a triangle is 180.
10. The measure of the exterior angle of a triangle is equal to the sum of the measures of the two remote interior angles.
11. always
12. never
13. $\overline{BC}$; $\overline{CD}$; $\angle ECB$
14. d and f
15. 70°, 50°, 60°
16. $\overline{JK} \cong \overline{QR}$, $\overline{KL} \cong \overline{RS}$, $\overline{JL} \cong \overline{QS}$

17. $x = 52$, $y = 23$
18. $y = 52$
19. $x = 77$
20. $x = 128$, $y = 45$
21. If all three pairs of the sides of two triangles are congruent, then the triangles are congruent.; True
22. If a triangle has two acute angles, then it is a right triangle.; False
23. **(1)** $\overline{JK} \perp \overline{KL}$, $\overline{JM} \perp \overline{ML}$, $\angle KJL \cong \angle MJL$ (Given)
 (2) $\angle K$ and $\angle M$ are right angles. (Perpendicular lines intersect to form right angles.)
 (3) $\angle K \cong \angle M$ (All right angles are congruent.)
 (4) $\overline{JL} \cong \overline{JL}$ (Reflexive)
 (5) $\triangle JKL \cong \triangle JML$ (A.A.S.)

24. **(1)** $\overline{AF} \perp \overline{BD}$, $\overline{CE} \perp \overline{BD}$ (Given)
 (2) $\angle AFB$ and $\angle CED$ are right angles. (Perpendicular lines intersect to form right angles.)
 (3) $\triangle ABF$ and $\triangle CDE$ are right triangles. (Definition of right triangle)
 (4) $BE = BF + FE$ and $FD = DE + FE$ (Betweenness of Points)
 (5) $BE = FD$ (Given)

(6) $BF + FE$
$= DE + FE$
(Substitution)
(7) $BF = DE$
(Subtraction)
(8) $AB = CD$ (Given)
(9) $\triangle ABF \cong \triangle CDE$
(H.L.)

Chapter 6 Test

1. True
2. False
3. altitude
4. sum; remote
5. Side-Side-Side
6. $\angle IGH$ and $\angle GIH$
7. $\overline{FG}$ and $\overline{IG}$
8.

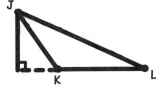

9.

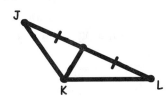

10. H.L.
11. None
12. A.A.S.
13. 88°, 46°, 46°
14. If two lines form congruent alternate interior angles with a transversal, then the lines are parallel.
15. Converse of Base Angles Theorem
16. $x = 25$
17. $x = 14$, $y = 55$
18. $x = 25$, $y = 10$

19. 22.5°
20. 133°, 47°
21. If a triangle has one angle that is greater than 90°, then it is obtuse; true
22. If two sides of a triangle are congruent (equal), then the angles opposite those sides are congruent (equal); true
23. **(1)** $\overline{KM} \parallel \overline{JH}$,
$\overline{KM} \cong \overline{JH}$,
$\overline{JK} \cong \overline{KL}$ (Given)
(2) $\angle HJK \cong$
$\angle MKL$ (If parallel lines are cut by a transversal, then corresponding angles are congruent.)
(3) $\triangle HJK \cong$
$\triangle MKL$ (S.A.S.)
(4) $\angle JKH \cong$
$\angle KLM$
(C.P.C.T.C.)
(5) $\overline{HK} \parallel \overline{ML}$ (If two lines form congruent corresponding angles with a transversal, then the lines are parallel.)
24. **(1)** $\triangle ABC$,
$\overline{CA} \cong \overline{CB}$, altitudes
$\overline{AD}$ and $\overline{BE}$
(Given)
(2) $\angle ADB$ and $\angle BEA$ are right angles. (Definition of altitude)

(3) $\angle ADB \cong \angle BEA$
(All right angles are congruent.)
(4) $\angle ABC \cong \angle BAC$
(Base Angles Theorem)
(5) $\overline{AB} \cong \overline{AB}$
(Reflexive)
(6) $\triangle ADB \cong \triangle BEA$
(A.A.S.)
(7) $\overline{AD} \cong \overline{BE}$
(C.P.C.T.C.)

Chapter 7 Test

1. False
2. True
3. multiplying; dividing
4. If b, then a
5. If not b, then not a
6. If not a, then not b
7. **a.** No; **b.** Yes
8. **a.** Greater than 5 and less than 9; **b.** Greater than 9 and less than 33
9. **(1)** $8x + 23 > 7$
(Addition Property of Inequality)
(2) $8x > -16$
(Subtraction Property of Inequality)
(3) $x > -2$ (Division Property of Inequality)
10. **(1)** $-\frac{1}{2}y \le 4$
(Addition Property of Inequality)
(2) $y \ge -8$
(Multiplication Property of Inequality)
11. 32°, 32°, 116°
12. 10°, 80°, 90°
13. Converse: If Mike lives in Hawaii, then

he lives in Honolulu;
false
Inverse: If Mike does
not live in Honolulu,
then he does not live
in Hawaii; false
Contrapositive: If
Mike does not live in
Hawaii, then he does
not live in Honolulu;
true

14. Converse: If two
angles are congruent,
then they are both
right angles; false.
Inverse: If two angles
are not both right
angles, then they are
not congruent; false.
Contrapositive: If two
angles are not
congruent, then they
are not both right
angles; true.

15. Triangle Inequality
Postulate

16. Exterior Angle
Inequality Theorem

17. If Unequal Angles,
then Unequal Sides

18. $\angle I$

19. $m + n = 140$

20. $x = 7.5$ and $y = 75$

21. $x = 42$

22. $a = 85$

23. (1) $\overline{PQ} \cong \overline{PR}$ (Given)
(2) $\angle 3 \cong \angle 4$ (Base
Angles Theorem)
(3) $\overline{QR} \parallel \overline{ST}$ (Given)
(4) $\angle 1 \cong \angle 3$ and
$\angle 2 \cong \angle 4$ (If two
parallel lines are cut
by a trans-versal, then

corr-esponding
angles are
congruent.)
(5) $\angle 1 \cong \angle 4$
(Transitive or
Substitution)
(6) $\angle 1 \cong \angle 2$
(Transitive or
Substitution)
(7) $\overline{SP} \cong \overline{TP}$
(Converse Base
Angles Theorem)
(8) $\triangle SPT$ is
isosceles.
(Definition of
isosceles triangle)

24. (1) $IJ = KJ$
(Given)
(2) Either
$IL = LM$ or
$IL \neq LM$. Assume
$IL = LM$. (A
statement is either
true or false.)
(3) $m\angle 1 = m\angle 2$
(Base Angles
Theorem)
(4) $m\angle 1 > m\angle K$
(Exterior Angle
Inequality
Theorem)
(5) $m\angle 2 > m\angle K$
(Substitution)
(6) $m\angle JIK > m\angle 2$
(Whole Greater
than Its Part)
(7)
$m\angle JIK > m\angle K$
(Transitive)
(8) $IJ < KJ$ (If
Unequal Angles,
then Unequal
Sides)
(9) $IL \neq LM$
(Statement 8

contra-dicts the given
state-ment that
$IJ = KJ$. The
assumption made in
statement 2 must be
false. By elimination,
statement 9 must be
true.)

Chapter 8 Test

1. False
2. True
3. 360°
4. trapezoid
5. diagonals
6. parallel; one-half
7. parallelogram
8. Isosceles trapezoid
9. rhombus
10. always
11. sometimes
12. Converse: If a figure is
a parallelogram, then
it is a rhombus; false
Inverse: If a figure is
not a rhombus, then it
is not a parallelogram;
false
Contrapositive: If a
figure is not a
parallelogram, then it
is not a rhombus; true

13. Converse: If a figure is
not a square, then it is
not a rectangle; false
Inverse: If a figure is a
rectangle, then it is a
square; false
Contrapositive: If a
figure is a square, then
it is a rectangle; true

14. The diagonals of a
rhombus are perpen-
dicular to each other.

15. The diagonals of an isosceles trapezoid are congruent.

16. If one pair of opposite sides is both parallel and congruent, then a quadrilateral is a parallelogram.

17. $x = 3$, $y = 120$, $z = 120$

18. $x = 9$

19. $y = 75$

20. $m\angle R = 110$, $m\angle S = 70$

21. $\angle G$

22. $m\angle K = 35$ and $m\angle L = 105$

23. **(1)** Rectangle *EJHG* (Given)
    (2) $\overline{EJ} \cong \overline{GH}$ (Both pairs of opposite sides of a rectangle are congruent.)
    (3) $\angle J \cong \angle G$ (Both pairs of opposite angles of a rectangle are congruent.)
    (4) $\overline{JI} \cong \overline{FG}$ (Given)
    (5) $\triangle JEI \cong \triangle GHF$ (S.A.S.)
    (6) $\overline{EI} \cong \overline{HF}$ (C.P.C.T.C.)

24. **(1)** $\triangle NOP \cong \triangle QRP$ (Given)
    (2) $\overline{NO} \cong \overline{QR}$ (C.P.C.T.C.)
    (3) *N* is the midpoint of $\overline{MO}$. (Given)
    (4) $\overline{MN} \cong \overline{NO}$ (Definition of midpoint)

(5) $\overline{MN} \cong \overline{QR}$ (Transitive or substitution)
(6) $\angle O \cong \angle PRQ$ (C.P.C.T.C.)
(7) $\overline{MN} \parallel \overline{QR}$ (If two lines form congruent alternate interior angles, then the lines are parallel.)
(8) *MNQR* is a parallelogram. (If one pair of opposite sides is both parallel and congruent, then a quadrilateral is a parallelogram.)

Chapter 9 Test

1. True
2. True
3. pentagon; hexagon
4. $\dfrac{360}{n}$ or $180 -$ the measure of each interior angle
5. $180(n - 2)$
6. hexagon, convex
7. pentagon, concave
8. nonagon, convex
9. 9 diagonals

10. 14 diagonals

11. Regular hexagon; interior: $120°$; exterior: $60°$

12. Regular decagon; interior: $144°$; exterior: $36°$

13. $360°$

14. always

15. never

16. Converse: If a figure is equilateral, then it is a regular polygon.; false.
    Inverse: If a figure is not a regular polygon, then it is not equilateral.; false
    Contrapositive: If a figure is not equilateral, then it is not a regular polygon.; true

17. 34

18. 126

19. $x + y = 170$

20. $x = 125$

21. $a + b + c + d = 230$

22. $x = 5$, $y = 6$

23. **(1)** *GCDE* is a rectangle. (Given)
    (2) $\overline{CE} \cong \overline{GD}$ (The diagonals of a rectangle are congruent.)
    (3) *GCEF* is a parallelogram. (Given)

(4) $\overline{CE} \cong \overline{GF}$ (If a quadrilateral is a parallelogram, then both pairs of opposite sides are congruent.)
(5) $\overline{GD} \cong \overline{GF}$ (Transitive)
(6) $\triangle GDF$ is isosceles. (Definition of isosceles triangle)

24. (1) $PQRS$ is a parallelogram. (Given)
(2) $\overline{PQ} \cong \overline{RS}$ (If a quadrilateral is a parallelogram, then both pairs of opposite sides are congruent.)
(3) $\angle P \cong \angle R$ (If a quadrilateral is a parallelogram, then both pairs of opposite angles are congruent.)
(4) $\overline{TQ} \perp \overline{QR}$, $\overline{US} \perp \overline{PS}$ (Given)
(5) $\angle TQR$ and $\angle PSU$ are right angles. (Perpendicular lines intersect to form right angles.)
(6) $\overline{QR} \parallel \overline{PS}$ (Definition of parallelogram)
(7) $\angle QTP$ and $\angle SUR$ are right angles. (If two parallel lines are cut by a transversal, then their alternate interior angles are congruent.)
(8) $\angle QTP \cong \angle SUR$ (All right angles are congruent.)

(9) $\triangle PQT \cong \triangle RSU$ (A.A.S.)

Chapter 10 Test
1. True
2. False
3. proportion
4. parallel
5. similar
6. **a.** Yes; **b.** Yes; **c.** No
7. $r = 9$
8. 8
9. $\dfrac{IL}{JL} = \dfrac{7}{3}$; $\dfrac{IM}{KM} = \dfrac{7}{3}$; sides are divided proportionally
10. 30 feet
11. 32 cm
12. S.S.S. Similarity
13. Converse of definition of similar figures
14. No
15. S.S.S. Similarity
16. A.A. Similarity
17. S.A.S. Similarity
18. 6
19. $y = 38$
20. $y = 30$
21. $MO = 12$, $PR = 3$
22. $PN = 3$, $IM = 5$
23. **(1)** $\overline{MN} \cong \overline{NO}$ (Given)
(2) $\angle M \cong \angle O$ (Base Angles Theorem)
(3) $\overline{GH} \perp \overline{MO}$, $\overline{PQ} \perp \overline{MO}$ (Given)

(4) $\angle GHO$ and $\angle PQM$ are right angles. (Perpendicular lines intersect to form right angles.)
(5) $\angle GHO \cong \angle PQM$ (All right angles are congruent.)
(6) $\triangle GHO \sim \triangle PQM$ (A.A. Similarity)

24. (1) $\triangle ORC \sim \triangle FEH$ (Given)
(2) $m\angle ORC = m\angle FEH$ (Converse of definition of similar triangles)
(3) $\dfrac{1}{2}m\angle ORC = \dfrac{1}{2}m\angle FEH$ (Multiplication)
(4) $\overline{RT}$ bisects $\angle ORC$, and $\overline{EG}$ bisects $\angle FEH$ (Given)
(5) $\dfrac{1}{2}m\angle ORC = m\angle TRC$ and $\dfrac{1}{2}m\angle FEH = m\angle GEH$ (Definition of angle bisector)
(6) $m\angle TRC = m\angle GEH$ (Substitution)
(7) $m\angle C = m\angle H$ (Converse of definition of similar triangles)
(8) $\triangle RTC \sim \triangle EGH$ (A.A. Similarity)

160

Chapter 11 Test
1. True
2. False
3. opposite; adjacent
4. similar
5. Pythagorean triple
6. $5\sqrt{3}$, 8.66
7. $8\sqrt{2}$, 11.31
8. Yes
9. No
10. $x = 4$
11. $x = 12$
12. $x = 10$
13. $y = 17.30$
14. 0.47
15. 0.91
16. 11.55
17. 6.43
18. 13 feet
19. $x = 18$
20. $y = 10\sqrt{2}$
21. 19.59 meters
22. 890.99 miles
23. (1) $\Delta FCE \sim \Delta HID$ (Given)
(2) $\angle CEF \cong \angle IDH$ (Converse of definition of similar triangles)
(3) $\overline{GD}$ bisects $\angle IDF$ (Given)
(4) $\angle IDH \cong \angle HDC$ (Definition of angle bisector)
(5) $\angle CEF \cong \angle HDC$ (Transitive or Substitution)
(6) $\angle FCE \cong \angle HCD$ (Pairs of vertical angles are congruent.)
(7) $\Delta FCE \sim \Delta HCD$ (A.A. Similarity)
24. (1) $PCDE$ is a parallelogram. (Given)

(2) $\overline{PC} \cong \overline{ED}$ and $\overline{PE} \cong \overline{CD}$ (Opposite sides of a parallelogram are congruent.)
(3) $\overline{PC} \parallel \overline{ED}$ and $\overline{PE} \parallel \overline{CD}$ (Definition of parallelogram)
(4) $\angle FPC \cong \angle GDE$ and $\angle FPE \cong \angle GDC$ (If two parallel lines are cut by a transversal, then their alternate interior angles are congruent.))
(5) $\overline{PF} \cong \overline{DG}$ (Given)
(6) $\Delta PFC \cong \Delta DGE$ and $\Delta PFE \cong \Delta DGC$ (S.A.S.)
(7) $\overline{FE} \cong \overline{GC}$ and $\overline{GE} \cong \overline{FC}$ (C.P.C.T.C.)
(8) $FCGE$ is a parallelogram (If both pairs of opposite sides are congruent, then a quadrilateral is a parallelogram.)

Chapter 12 Test
1. True
2. False
3. secant
4. semicircle
5. sum
6. secant line
7. tangent line
8. radius
9. 124°
10. 193°
11. 9π
12. 14π
13. 62.5°
14. 46°
15. 6
16. 5
17. $x = 6$
18. $y = 116$
19. $x = 12\sqrt{3}$
20. $d = 65$
21. If a line through the center of a circle is perpendicular to a chord, it also bisects the chord.
22. In the same circle, chords equidistant from the center of the circle are congruent.
23. (1) $\overline{IK}$ and $\overline{IM}$ are secant segments. (Given)
(2) $IK \times IJ = IM \times IL$ (If two secant segments are drawn to a circle from the same exterior point, then the product of the lengths of one secant segment and its external segment is equal to the product of the lengths of the other secant segment and its external segment.)
(3) $IK = IM$ (Given)
(4) $IM \times IJ = IM \times IL$ (Substitution)
(5) $IJ = IL$ (Division)

24. **(1)** Draw radii $\overline{OR}$ and $\overline{OS}$.(Two points determine a unique straight line.)
(2) $\overline{OR} \cong \overline{OS}$ (All radii of the same circle are congruent.)
(3) $\overline{PQ} \perp \overline{RS}$ (Given)
(4) $\angle OTR$ and $\angle OTS$ are right angles. (Perpendicular lines intersect to form right angles.)
(5) ΔOTR and ΔOTS are right triangles. (Definition of right triangle)
(6) $\overline{OT} \cong \overline{OT}$ (Reflexive)
(7) $\Delta OTR \cong \Delta OTS$ (H.L.)
(8) $\angle ROP \cong \angle SOP$ (C.P.C.T.C.)
(9) $m\angle ROP = m\widehat{RP}$ and $m\angle SOP = m\widehat{PS}$ (The degree measure of a minor arc is the measure of its central angle.)
(10) $\widehat{RP} \cong \widehat{PS}$ (Substitution)

Chapter 13 Test

1. False
2. True
3. the two diagonals
4. square
5. triangle
6. 105 sq. in.
7. 1200 cm^2
8. 24
9. 36

10. 18
11. 112
12. 88
13. 12
14. 78
15. 153 cm^2
16. 60 in.^{2}
17. 112 m^2
18. 18 ft^2
19. 252π
20. 24π
21. 1080
22. $x = 6$
23. **(1)** $\overline{LK} \cong \overline{IJ}$ (Given)
(2) $m\widehat{LK} = m\widehat{IJ}$ (If two chords of the same circle are congruent, then their minor arcs are congruent.)
(3) $m\widehat{JK} = m\widehat{JK}$ (Reflexive)
(4) $m\widehat{LK} + m\widehat{JK} = m\widehat{IJ} + m\widehat{JK}$ (Addition)
(5) $m\widehat{LJ} = m\widehat{IK}$ (Arc Addition Postulate)
(6) $\overline{LJ} \cong \overline{IK}$ (If two minor arcs of the same circle are congruent, then their intersected chords are congruent.)
24. **(1)** $\overline{PR}$ is tangent to $\odot O$ at P and $\overline{QR}$ is tangent to $\odot O$ at Q. (Given)
(2) $\overline{PR} \cong \overline{QR}$ (If two tangent

segments are drawn to a circle from the same exterior point, then they are congruent.)
(3) $\angle RPO$ and $\angle RQO$ are right angles. (If a radius is drawn to the point of tangency of a tangent line, then the radius is perpendicular to the tangent line.)
(4) $\angle RPO \cong \angle RQO$ (All right angles are congruent.)
(5) $\overline{RO} \cong \overline{RO}$ (Reflexive)
(6) $\Delta RPO \cong \Delta RQO$ (H.L.)
(7) $\angle PRO \cong \angle QRO$ (C.P.C.T.C.)
(8) $\overrightarrow{RS}$ bisects $\angle PRQ$. (Definition of an angle bisector.)

Chapter 14 Test

1. False
2. True
3. area of the base; altitude
4. altitude; perimeter; area of a base
5. one-third; $V = \dfrac{1}{3}\pi r^2 a$
6. 48π
7. $484 - 121\pi$
8. $6\pi - 9\sqrt{3}$
9. $S.A. = 416$ in.^{2}; $V = 480$ in.^{3}
10. $S.A. = 964$ cm^2; $V = 1{,}872$ cm^3

11. (triangular) pyramid
12. oblique pentagonal prism
13. 228
14. 485
15. 324π
16. 320
17. 16,261
18. $2,187\pi$
19. 105
20. $n = 100$
21. $c = 45$
22. $64:1$
23. **(1)** $\overline{KL} \parallel \overline{IJ}$ (Given)
 (2) $m\angle KLI = m\angle JIL$ (If two parallel lines are cut by a transversal, then their alternate interior angles are equal.)
 (3) $m\angle KLI = \frac{1}{2}m\widehat{IK}$ and $m\angle JIL = \frac{1}{2}m\widehat{LJ}$ (An inscribed angle is equal in measure to one-half the measure of its intercepted arc.)
 (4) $\frac{1}{2}m\widehat{IK} = \frac{1}{2}m\widehat{LJ}$ (Substitution)
 (5) $m\widehat{IK} = m\widehat{LJ}$ (Multiplication)
 (6) $\widehat{IK} \cong \widehat{JL}$ (Congruent arcs have equal measures.)
24. **(1)** $JKLMN$ is a regular polygon. (Given)
 (2) $\angle OPK$ and $\angle OPL$ are right angles. (Definition of apothem of a regular polygon)
 (3) $\overline{OK} \cong \overline{OL}$ (Definition of radius of a regular polygon)
 (4) $\overline{OP} \cong \overline{OP}$ (Reflexive)
 (5) $\triangle KPO \cong \triangle LPO$ (H.L.)
 (6) $\overline{KP} \cong \overline{LP}$ (C.P.C.T.C.)
 (7) $\overline{OP}$ bisects $\overline{KL}$. (Definition of segment bisector)

Chapter 15 Test
1. False
2. True
3. x-coordinate; y-coordinate
4. negative reciprocals
5. $y = mx + b$; slope; y-intercept
6. $H(-2,3)$ and $F(2,-2)$
7. $P(-a,a)$ and $Q(0,a)$
8. $12.5\pi - 24$
9. 16
10. $\left(\dfrac{a-c}{2}, \dfrac{b+d}{2}\right)$
11. $\left(0, -\dfrac{5}{2}\right)$
12. 3
13. $\sqrt{a^2 + c^2}$
14. I, K, J
15. Line E: $-\dfrac{7}{6}$; Line F: 1

16. 816 cm^2
17. 720
18. $y - 8 = -1(x+3)$
19. $y + 5 = -\dfrac{3}{2}(x-2)$
20. $y = 5\sqrt{13}$
21. $r = 3\sqrt{2}$
22. $\sqrt{(x-m)^2 + (y-n)^2}$
23. The lengths of the horizontal legs are $PS = p$ and $QR = p+q-q = p$, so $PS = QR$ by substitution. By the distance formula, $PQ = \sqrt{(q-0)^2 + (r-0)^2} = \sqrt{q^2 + r^2}$ and $RS = \sqrt{(p+q-p)^2 + (r-0)^2} = \sqrt{q^2 + r^2}$, so by substitution $PQ = SR$.
24. **(1)** $\overline{HJ} \parallel \overline{FG}$ (Given)
 (2) Draw chord HG (Two points determine a unique straight line.)
 (3) $m\angle JHG = m\angle HGF$ (If two parallel lines are cut by a transversal, then their alternate interior angles are equal.)
 (4) $m\angle JHG = \frac{1}{2}m\widehat{JG}$ & $m\angle HGF = \frac{1}{2}m\widehat{HF}$ (An inscribed angle is equal in measure to one-half the measure of its intercepted arc.)

(5) $\frac{1}{2}m\widehat{JG} = \frac{1}{2}m\widehat{HF}$ (Substitution or transitive)

(6) $m\widehat{JG} = m\widehat{HF}$ (Multiplication)

(7) $m\widehat{FG} = m\widehat{FG}$ (Reflexive)

(8) $m\widehat{JG} + m\widehat{FG} = m\widehat{HF} + m\widehat{FG}$ (Addition)

(9) $m\widehat{JGF} = m\widehat{JG} + m\widehat{FG}$ and $m\widehat{HFG} = m\widehat{HF} + m\widehat{FG}$ (Arc Addition Postulate)

(10) $m\widehat{JGF} = m\widehat{HFG}$ (Substitution)

(11) $\angle EHJ \cong \angle EJH$ (Inscribed angles that intercept congruent arcs are congruent.)

(12) $\overline{JE} \cong \overline{HE}$ (Converse of Base Angles Theorem)